MW00575842

Creative Choice
In Hypnosis

CREATIVE CHOICE IN HYPNOSIS

THE SEMINARS, WORKSHOPS, AND LECTURES OF MILTON H. ERICKSON

VOLUME IV

By
Milton H. Erickson

Edited by
Ernest L. Rossi
Margaret O. Ryan

IRVINGTON PUBLISHERS, INC.
NEW YORK

Irvington Publishers, Inc.,
Executive offices: 522 E. 82nd Street, Suite 1, New York, NY 10028
Customer service and warehouse in care of: Integrated Distribution
Services, 195 McGregor St, Manchester, NH 03102, (603) 669-5933

Library of Congress Cataloging-in-Publication Data

Erickson, Milton H.
    Creative choice in hypnosis / by Milton H. Erickson ; edited by
Ernest L. Rossi, Margaret O. Ryan.
        p.   cm.   — (The Seminars, workshops, and lectures of Milton
H. Erickson ; v. 4)
    Includes bibliographical references and index.
    ISBN 0-8290-2418-2 (Includes audio cassette)
    ISBN 0-8290-3152-9 (Without audio cassette)
    1. Hypnotism—Therapeutic use. 2. Double bind (Psychology)—
Therapeutic use. I. Rossi, Ernest Lawrence. II. Ryan, Margaret O.
(Margaret O'Loghlin) III. Title. IV. Series: Erickson, Milton H.
Selections. 1982 ; v. 4.
RC495.E712   1992
616.89' 162—dc20   91-656
                                              CIP

First Printing 1992
1 3 5 7 9 10 8 6 4 2

Printed in the United States of America

Contents

Prefatory Notes vii
Introduction ix

Part I
Creative Choice Versus
Manipulation In Hypnosis 1
(This section is a transcription of the audio tape that accompanies this volume.)

Part II
Facilitating Inner Work
Through "Manipulation" 95

Part III
Hypnotic Induction
And Suggestion:
Creative Choice In Sensory
Experience And Behavior 133

Part IV
Choice, Paradox, And
Meaning In Hypnotherapy 159

Part V
Creative Choice With
Therapeutic Double Binds 199

Part VI
Expanding Human Potentials
In Illness And Injury 211

Part VII
Creative Choice In Therapeutic Hypnosis 225

Footnotes 251
References 255
Index 263

Prefatory Notes

Regarding References

Because of the informal nature of the material presented in this series, the editors have used footnotes placed at the end of the book. However, Part VII utilizes the standard APA format for referencing because of the scholarly orientation of the material.

Regarding the Index

While the editors continue to disavow any effort to systematize Erickson's material in these volumes, we have made a careful effort to catalogue the subject matter in two ways. First we have provided frequent headings which appear on every page or two to focus attention on the major theme that Erickson is presenting. *These headings are the editors' efforts to catalogue—not Erickson's.* The contents in these headings are then used to select key subject words for the index. *The index is thus the key to the subject matter in these volumes* and can serve as a reference tool for interested readers.

Regarding the Commentary

Any added commentary by the editors was written after Erickson's death and without the benefit of prior discussion with him.

A Note to the Reader

We are pleased that, for the first time, both major series of Erickson's work—*The Seminars, Workshops and Lectures of Milton H. Erickson* and *The Collected Papers of Milton H. Erickson on Hypnosis* will be available in bookstores around the world. For readers who are just beginning to learn about Erickson, we would like to answer some frequently asked questions.

Each series of books presents a unique and valuable facet of Erickson's contribution. *The Collected Papers*, edited by Ernest Rossi, includes all of Erickson's published and previously unpublished papers on hypnosis. These four volumes reflect one of the most innovative bodies of work in the history of therapeutic hypnosis and psychology.

The *Seminars* series, co-edited by Ernest Rossi and Margaret Ryan, provides never-before-published transcriptions of many of Erickson's teaching seminars, lectures and workshops. Because his lectures are more conversational and anecdotal than his papers, we recommend that the general reader begin with one of the *Seminars* volumes. Perhaps most appropriate would be the first volume, *Healing in Hypnosis*, which contains a fascinating biographical chapter revealing the many important events of Erickson's life that contributed to the development of his ideas. The audio cassettes that accompany each of the *Seminars* volumes are also highly recommend for those of you exploring Erickson's ideas for the first time. There is simply no substitute for hearing his inimitable voice firsthand and experiencing the glint of wit and humor that flashes throughout his words.

We have been asked if you need to have experienced hypnotherapy with a therapist in order to benefit from Erickson's *Papers* and *Seminars*. The answer is no. There is much to be learned about life in general from reading these volumes, even if you've had no prior experience with hypnotherapy. Erickson is famous for his unprecedented and often humorous approaches to facilitating family life through all the stages of development, from childhood and adolescence through the career years and the senior years. The brilliance of Erickson's work can be found in his ability to utilize each person's unique inner resources and abilities for coping creatively with the real problems of everyday life. Readers often experience a stimulation of their own personal potentials simply by reading Erickson's stories, tales, anecdotes, and case studies.

Erickson continually expressed an exuberant delight in living, even under conditions of hardship with which he was well acquainted. Born with a number of perceptual handicaps, he endured two bouts of polio—first, during his adolescence, and later in his early fifties. He was in a wheelchair throughout much of his later life and learned to use the healing methods of self-hypnosis to deal with these handicaps and to uncover ways of experiencing living at more profound levels. His delight and joy in teaching these methods of self-healing are as contagious as his belief in the fathomless possibilities of the human spirit.

For Erickson, hypnosis was one way of tapping into those possibilities and experiencing healing through self-empowerment. The insights in Erickson's work can become the catalyst for much creative change and growth. His genius has left a legacy that can enable us to utilize our own life experience and unconscious learnings to re-create our lives in new and meaningful ways.

Ernest L. Rossi
Margaret O. Ryan

Introduction

Our title, *Creative Choice in Hypnosis*, will seem paradoxical to many prospective readers. It is the reverse of the popular but erroneous view of hypnosis as a method of manipulating and programming others. To understand this paradox, we will explore the fundamental issues of mind-body healing as well as creativity, free will, and manipulation in human affairs. With many rich illustrations from the case histories of the generally acknowledged "master hypnotist" of our time, we will come to grips with provocative questions such as:

- How is it possible to facilitate free will and creative choice in ourselves and others?
- How do we reframe problems into opportunities and illness into health?
- How do we convert negative attitudes associated with learning problems, obesity, stuttering, chronic pain, sexual dysfunctions, and a variety of obsessive-compulsive habits into positive possibilities for cure?
- How do we make children obey? That is, how do we help children deal happily and effectively with their own difficulties?
- What is the Zen of therapeutic suggestion? Can enlightenment come from the barrel of a double bind?

In this fourth volume of Milton H. Erickson's *Seminars, Workshops, and Lectures,* we celebrate the exploration of these and many other controversial questions about his new and eminently practical approaches to healing and liberating the human spirit. These explorations will require a deepening appreciation of the man and his struggle to express his quixotic contributions.

In retrospect we can now appreciate Milton H. Erickson as a transition figure in the history of hypnosis: His work clearly illustrates the shift from the authoritarian to the permissive approach, from direct to indirect suggestion, from programming the subject with the therapist's views to the therapeutic utilization of the subject's own inner resources for healing and development.

Even a cursory review of Erickson's early papers, however, reveals a personal penchant for *directing* the subject (*albeit* in an indirect manner). This is particularly evident in his early papers on the induction of hypnosis (Volume I of *Collected Papers*) and the hypnotic alteration of psychological processes (Volumes II and III of *Collected Papers*). Even in his later papers on psychotherapy (Volume IV of *Collected Papers*) and in my later recordings of his therapeutic work (Erickson & Rossi, 1979, 1981, 1989; Erickson, Rossi, & Rossi, 1976), however, he displayed his genius in utilizing the patient's own mental mechanisms to facilitate therapeutic goals in a manner that was still firmly directed by him.

With the help of my constant prodding, Erickson acknowledged that he could not predict with certainty what the outcomes of his indirect suggestions would be. Although he liked to feel he was in the driver's seat, he frequently stated that it was best simply to recognize and facilitate the patient's own proclivities.

This is the deepest sense in which Erickson was a transition figure: Personally, he was still imbued with the directive and authoritarian ideology of the past, yet his own innovative brilliance was to be found in his accessing and utilization of the patient's inherent potentials to function in his/her own way.

Nowhere is this authoritarian-permissive paradox more evident than in Erickson's use of the double bind (Erickson & Rossi, 1975/1980) as illustrated in this volume. He claimed to have been using double and triple binds on subjects long before Bateson's group (Bateson, Jackson, Haley, & Weakland, 1956) coined the term. Erickson spoke with great relish about the double bind and used Kubie's psychoanalytic concept of "illusory choice" to define it. In this conceptualization, the double bind was a way of giving a subject the *illusion of choice:* Erickson would arrange the situation so that whatever choice the patient selected would further his or her therapeutic goals. He found it humorous that patients thought they had freedom of choice even when, in effect, he was compelling them to make a therapeutic choice. In this sense I believe the spirit of Haley's analysis of how Erickson used the double bind to direct therapy is correct (Haley, 1963).

I simply do not like this way of conceptualizing the double bind as a means of *compelling* an "illusory choice," however. I just don't think this is the correct attitude for the hypnotherapist of the future; it is not the right way to go about doing therapy. It places undue stress on both the patient and therapist: The therapist is supposed to be omniscient in knowing what is good for the patient; the patient's spontaneous creativity and new development paradoxically is supposed to be known and directed by the therapist. In other words, the "illusory choice" conception of the double bind contradicts the *sui generis* creative process of psychotherapy.

I found a way out of this dilemma in my first paper on the double bind, co-authored with Erickson, by emphasizing that in spite of the "illusory choice" aspect of the double bind, Erickson actually used it in a way that did give the subject the ultimate freedom of creative choice. I offered an interpretation of the *"therapeutic double bind"* as a "free choice among comparable alternatives" rather than as a bind of illusory choice. I believe this view also framed the ethics and limitations in our use of the therapeutic double bind as follows (Erickson & Rossi, 1975/1980, pp. 477-478):

> As Erickson indicated in his early exploration of the double bind, there are significant limitations in its use. When the double bind is used in a therapeutic milieu, there is a positive feeling associated with the therapeutic metalevel which determines that some choice will be made. Because of this basically positive context or metalevel, patients will accept one alter-

native even if they do not care for any. They will accept their bitter medicine, if it is good for them.

When a free choice among comparable alternatives is offered without a positive metalevel structuring the situation, the subjects are free to refuse all choices. If we walk up to a stranger and ask, "Will you give me a dime or a dollar?", we will obviously be turned down more often than not because there is no metalevel binding the stranger to accept one of the offered alternatives. If the stranger happens to be charitable, however, this characteristic of charitableness may function as a positive metalevel that will determine that we get at least a dime.

When the relationship or metalevel is *competitive* or *negative,* however, we can always expect a rejection of all the double bind alternatives offered on the primary level. The competitive situation of a debate yields negative results, as Erickson found, unless the alternatives favor the other side. In the utterly negative situation of war or harm, "Do you want a punch in the nose or a kick in the teeth?", we can expect universal rejection of the alternatives. *The therapeutic usefulness of the double bind, then, is limited to situations that are structured by a positive metalevel.* The structuring presence of a positive metalevel [a constructive or therapeutic context], together with free choice on the primary level, also define the ethical use of the double bind.

This contrast in the conception of the double bind as *illusory choice* or as a truly *creative choice* among comparable alternatives is one that is very difficult for critics to understand. Recently, for example, a reviewer of my book, *The Psychobiology of Mind-Body Healing* (Rossi, 1986b), had this to say (Spiegel, 1988):

> On p. 78, there is a troubling statement: "This implication . . . gives the patient's unconscious processes free choice." Free choice is not given, and this

kind of patronizing, 'bestowing of choice' on patients reflects a style that permeates the writing of this and many other Ericksonian books that will make some readers, and presumably as many patients, extremely uncomfortable.

It is true that free choice is not given by the therapist. However, I believe that the therapist can facilitate free choice within the patient. Free choice may even be inherent in the way the unconscious-conscious process operates, even though most of us do not realize it. The recent research of Libet (1985; Rossi, 1988) documents how what we experience mentally as "mind, consciousness, and free will" is actually about 0.2 seconds behind the "readiness potential" that indicates when a voluntary act will arise. Libet interprets his research on the relationship between unconscious and conscious processes and free will as follows (Libet, 1985, p. 529):

> The experimental finding led us to the conclusion that *voluntary acts can be initiated by unconscious cerebral processes before conscious intention appears* but that conscious control over the actual motor performance of the acts remains possible. I propose the thesis that conscious volitional control may operate not to initiate the volitional process but to select and control it, either by permitting or triggering the final motor outcome of the unconsciously initiated process or by vetoing the progression to actual motor activation.
>
> . . . *The finding should therefore be taken not as being antagonistic to free will but rather as affecting the view of how free will might operate. Processes associated with individual responsibility and free will would "operate" not to initiate a voluntary act but to select and control volitional outcomes.*
>
> . . . The concept of conscious veto or blockage of the motor performance or specific intentions to act is in general accord with certain religious and humanistic views of ethical behavior and individual re-

sponsibility. "Self-control" of the acting out of one's intentions is commonly advocated; in the present terms this would operate by conscious selection or control of whether the unconsciously initiated final volitional process will be implemented in action. [Italics added]

From the perspective offered by Libet's experimental findings, I would now interpret the therapeutic double bind as facilitating the process of creative choice by asking us to suspend the expression of habitual attitudes and mental sets for a short period of time. These habitual attitudes are typically high on our response hierarchies and tend to be expressed first in a choice situation. However, these very attitudes often contain "learned limitations" that are blocking the autonomous, *sui generis*, and creative problem-solving capacities *"initiated by unconscious cerebral processes before conscious intention appears."*

By suspending our habitual attitudes, we are momentarily withholding our "conscious veto or blockage" and thus permitting unconscious cerebral processes to operate with a bit more freedom to create and express the new. We can then enjoy a broader palette of choices for voluntary expression. We will have a "free choice among comparable alternatives," which is the way I conceptualize the therapeutic double bind. When the double bind is used in this way, it can facilitate creative choice. It is for this reason that we decided to entitle this volume *Creative Choice in Hypnosis*.

Ernest Lawrence Rossi
Malibu

PART I

Creative Choice Versus Manipulation In Hypnosis[1]

The Nature of Therapeutic Hypnosis

Hypnosis as the "Meeting of Two Minds";
Utilization of Everyday Life Phenomena

Ordinarily we look upon hypnosis as something that results from the induction of a hypnotic trance. Our concept of the induction of hypnotic trance dates back to 1776 and even earlier. There is a great, great tendency to make use of certain words, and certain phrases, and certain pauses, and certain ideas to induce a trance—and we have all manner of trance inductions. But the thing you ought to consider is that hypnosis is essentially a matter of the communication of ideas and understandings of one person to another, with understandings of the other person's ideas and understandings, so that you have a meeting of two minds for a single purpose: namely, the welfare of the patient.

The second thing you ought to bear in mind is that in hypnosis you are using the phenomena of everyday life. All hypnotic phenomena can find their counterparts in everyday behavior; the only difference is that in hypnosis, everyday behavior is directed and controlled and utilized at a much greater extent. Amnesia, anesthesia, dissociations—all of those phenomena to which we are accustomed as a part of our daily living; our dissociation from our environment, our

1

recollection of long, long past events, the sudden flashes of memory that we get—those are [all] parts of everyday life. In hypnosis we simply utilize those [phenomena] in a directed and controlled and a much more prolonged fashion.

Attentional Differences between Hypnosis and Everyday Life

Trance With Or Without Awareness of It

Therefore, in utilizing the hypnotic techniques, the sole purpose is to address your subject in such a way that he is likely to give you *his* attention in a manner in which his attention is given to you, and is not given in the way that it is [given] in ordinary everyday life. In ordinary everyday life, as a part of the law of self-preservation (preservation of the species), we have a constant need to orient to our reality surroundings. We need to know where we are: We need to know whether we are in a room or outside; we need to know whether there are lights on, whether there are others present, and what is going on about us. From moment to moment, second to second, we are constantly aware of the fact that "somebody is sitting beside me, in front of me, behind me"; that there are lights on, that there are lights off, that there are walls, that there are lights in the ceiling, that there are microphones around, that there are glasses of water, that there are white tablecloths. We never content ourselves with one realization of that particular fact, but do we need to keep reminding ourselves of those items of reality?

Once we know those items of reality, we are secure and we are safe. But in ordinary everyday life, we are not in a protected situation. The problems of life cause a constant change in our environment. But when you seek out the dental office, the medical office, the psychologists's office, there you have a limited and restricted environment. You go there for a particular purpose, and because it is for a particular purpose, you do not need to keep noticing that there is carpet on part of the floor, that there is not carpeting on another part of the floor. You do not need to note that there are pictures on the wall, and different kinds of pictures, and that there are different kinds of lighting fixtures. You can devote your entire time, your entire energies, to the demands of that particular situation. But you have a lifetime of experience and a lifetime habit of dividing your attention in a wealth of ways.

Now the wild animal is always on the alert—eternal vigilance is the price of survival. But once that animal goes into its burrow and is safe and secure there, he shuts his eyes and he goes to sleep, and that is that. He gives no further attention, until there comes about a massive, disturbing stimulus. The same sort of thing should exist in your office. Your patient ought to enter your office and enter into a relationship with you (whether it is dental, medical, or psychological—no matter what the purpose of it is)—enter into that relationship so that the patient can give full attention to whatever is pertinent to the situation and not have the mind wandering from the picture on the wall, to the filing cabinet, to the paperweight on the table, and so on. Once you learn how to fixate your patient's attention and to hold that patient's attention, when you see it wandering [you can] just speak in such a fashion that the patient's attention comes back to the matter in hand. *Then you have that patient in a hypnotic trance, whether the patient knows it or doesn't know it.*

The Patient's Privilege of Choosing Hypnotic Amnesia

Not so long ago a patient said: "I am coming to you for therapy, but I certainly do not want any hypnosis used on me."

My statement was:

"You are coming for therapy, and since you are coming for therapy, I expect you will probably take therapy. And if you take therapy, it will be therapy that you take in accord with your own needs. I'll offer you the therapeutic understandings, and it is your privilege to take them in any way that you

3

wish. I don't know—because I don't know you and I don't know your needs—I don't know exactly how you will take the therapeutic ideas, the therapeutic aid I can give you."

Rossi: Erickson's phrase, "I don't know exactly how you will take the therapeutic ideas, the therapeutic aid I can give you," is highly characteristic of his indirect style. He is using a disarming truism ("I don't know") to open a *yes set* enabling the patient to accept the therapeutic ideas in any way possible for his or her individuality. The actual therapeutic suggestion, " . . . you will take the therapeutic ideas, the therapeutic aid I can give you," is *embedded* within the yes set. If the patient accepts the truism that Erickson "doesn't know," then the patient also will accept by *implication* the indirect suggestion, "you will take . . . the therapeutic aid I can give you."

We had a delightful two-hour conference. The patient was pleased and seemed to think that I knew what I was talking about, and that I had covered the problem fairly well. The next day the patient came into the office and said, "There is something awfully wrong here. I came to you, I was pleased, I left here feeling satisfied, but after I got to my motel room, I didn't remember a solitary thing that happened in the office. I have been laboring ever since to discover what on earth we had been talking about. What did I tell you? Did I tell you anything about myself? I know I spent two hours here, but I can only remember your introductory remarks, and that is all."
So I reminded the patient:

"You came for therapy. It was your privilege to take the therapy in any way that you wanted. Apparently you have decided that your way of taking therapy is first to take it at an unconscious level, and then after you have digested it at an unconscious level, you'll probably let it trickle then into your conscious mind, and then you will be consciously aware of it. Now, as for today, we have a two-hour appointment. I don't know what you are going to do. I don't know if when you leave this office, you are going to have a total amnesia for what occurred, or whether you are going to have a total memory. In fact, I don't think it is important. I think the important thing *is* that you reach some understanding of these things that have been troubling you for so long, and that's our task at hand."

Minimal Cues of Therapeutic Trance

Indirect Versus Direct Trance Induction

It was very easy for me to recognize immediately that, while the patient agreed with me consciously, the patient also agreed with me unconsciously. I noticed the patient's face smoothed out; I noticed the catalepsy of the facial musculature; I noticed the loss of the blink reflex, the loss of the swallowing reflex, the alternation in the respiratory rhythm, the failure of the mobility of the body, the readiness with which the patient would answer, precisely and specifically, the questions that I put to the patient. So I knew my patient had, without any training, without any effort on my part, simply given over to me full and complete attention, and had gone into a trance state.

Now, why shouldn't I do it that way instead of saying: "Now fixate on the spot on the wall, and let your lids get heavier and heavier, and let yourself feel relaxed. Direct your attention to your feet and the relaxation feeling there . . . the warmth and the heaviness . . . and so on. Watch that relaxation creep up your legs and up through your knees and thighs, and over your body, and the nice feeling of warmth and comfort in your hands."

If you get the patient interested in the things that are really vital to the patient, the patient automatically takes their attention away from things unrelated to the problem. I think

5

it is extremely important that every one of you learn the relaxation technique, the hand levitation technique, the eye closure technique, the person-tree-window technique, the confusion technique, the utilization technique, or any other technique that you wish. The reason for learning those techniques is to acquaint *you* with the need and the ability to recognize the pertinent points that you want to use when you deal with a patient at a therapeutic level. I think it is awfully important that you know when you are talking to a patient that you are holding your patient's attention to this one particular thing; that you are aware of that fact, and that you *hold* the patient's attention there, and then when you want to shift it somewhere else, you very carefully alter the tone of your voice and you shift the attention somewhere else. It isn't just the words that you say; it's your willingness to do the things that you do in ordinary everyday life.

Minimal Vocal and Body Cues
Versus Literal Verbal Meanings

I can remind you of Frank Bacon who became a star overnight. He played in the play called *Lightening*. I heard him, and then even though I couldn't afford it then, I went back and heard him again, and again, and again—even though I was a student wondering where I would get my next bit of cash to buy another 25-cent meal (there were such things in those days). What did Frank Bacon have to say on the stage in the play *Lightening*? He had exactly one word to say. He said, "NO," but he said it 16 times in 16 different ways, and it was the most delightful experience I ever had in my life—listening to a man saying NO, and giving it 16 different meanings! So I went to my room and I thought that over, and I studied it, and I wondered if ever I could learn to say NO with 16 different meanings. It is possible, because Frank Bacon demonstrated it and made his fame as an actor in that regard.

In hypnosis you ought to recognize that the way you say something conveys a tremendous amount, and that the words [themselves] have literally no meaning. It is the manner, the bearing, the attitude, the intonation, the inflection that carries the meaning.

"How do you do?"

I can think of being in the thank-you queue where we were all thanking our hostess for the very delightful dinner, and it was very charming to be in that long queue of guests who were thanking the hostess. She was always saying the appropriate, the gracious things to each who shook her by the hand. Being a little bit mischievous, I thought I would have a perfectly delightful time, and as I shook hands with her to say "Thank you for the very nice dinner," I told her: "Thank you very much. I thought those fried horses' tails were absolutely delicious, and could I have the recipe please?" She said, "I will be very pleased to send it to you."

I had used the right inflection—*the words meant nothing*. I did the right thing, I had the right attitude, the right bearing, the right manner, and the mere fact that I said "fried horses' tails" meant nothing so far as thanking her for the dinner. Margaret Mead happened to be with me at the time and she listened with a great deal of amusement to what I was saying to the hostess. She studied the hostess's face to see if the hostess actually heard what I said, because I had spoken very distinctly. Margaret Mead knew it, but the hostess heard the right tones, the right inflections, saw the right facial expressions—everything that was correct. I could have used any words I wanted to so long as I used the right expression.

Selecting Techniques Expressive of the Therapist's Personality

So it is in the use of hypnosis. You use not just words; you learn words, you learn the various techniques, and you study those techniques, and you study the meanings that those techniques convey to you. Then you select out of those various techniques (whether it is a hand levitation technique, the eye closure technique, or the body relaxation technique, or whatever technique it is) that type of meaning that is expressive of your personality. If you happen to be an exceedingly dynamic type of person, I don't think you ought to try to convey to your patient, so contrary to your nature: "I would like you to get tired . . . and sleepy . . . and sleepier . . . and sleepier," because your way of speaking is: "I'D LIKE YOU TO GET TIRED AND SLEEPY," so I think you ought to say:

"Take all the time that you want to go deeply into a trance. Go only as deeply as you want to go, and take all the time that is necessary, but you really don't need to waste any time at all. But take your time, and go deeply and quickly into a trance in the way that is most satisfying to you."

And so you are using your own dynamic personality, and you are conveying to the patient the same thing that the soft, gentle person says when he tells you:

"Now relax gently... feel at ease... be comfortable all over... and begin relaxing your feet, and your legs, and your thighs... and feel the comfort of your arms... and take all the time that you want to take."

Expanding the Therapist's Range of Expression

"Bulldog's" Experience with Autohypnosis;
Learning "Every Conceivable Technique"

I have offered you those two extremes. I would like to have you recognize that no one of you is bound to any one particular kind of technique. The person who thinks he is a vivacious, dynamic, and forceful person really ought to discover whether or not he can be a soft and gentle and permissive sort of person. I can think of a man who proudly told me that his nickname since early childhood had been "Bulldog," and that everybody called him Bulldog because when he spoke to somebody, he spoke to them in a bulldog fashion.

I asked him what luck he was having in this practice session putting his patients into a trance and he said, "None at all." I said, "Why don't you pick out a good bulldog to work on?" He asked me, "What do you mean by that?"

My statement was:

"I think the best bulldog I've seen in the audience today was one who told me his nickname was Bulldog. So tonight when you go to your room, sit down in front of the mirror and look at that bulldog, and really tell him off, and tell him to go into a trance, and keep him in a trance all night long. Show him who's boss!"

He woke up at 4:00 A.M. and he was utterly delighted to find out that he had induced an autohypnotic trance in himself, using his technique on himself. He said: "I don't ever want to put a patient into a trance that lasts from nine o'clock in the evening until 4:00 A.M. That isn't right. That isn't fair."

My statement was:

"Neither is that bulldog technique of yours you use on your patients. Why don't you use a gentle, little, soft-spoken voice on some of your patients?"

So Bulldog started using a softly spoken, gentle, permissive technique, and in his next practice session he had excellent results.

Rossi: Note the appropriateness of this *utilization* approach. Erickson's words, "Show him who's the boss!", *utilize* Bulldog's major way of presenting himself to the world—a lifelong personality pattern in which he obviously has much invested. Yet notice the ingeniously simple paradox that is involved in *utilizing* this person's dominant Bulldog personality to learn to become the reverse—"gentle, little, soft-spoken," when it is appropriate.

Now I want to encourage every one of you to learn every conceivable technique so that you can use it fluently, readily, and easily at the slightest opportunity. I'd like to have you also try to recognize what are the essential phenomena that you are using that technique for. One of them is that you don't want the patient looking at the wall and noticing the scratch on the wall up there, and the light [that] shows through; and then there are some sockets in the wall over there, and there is some carpet here, and there is some striped carpet out there, and a bare floor here, and there is an ashtray here. You don't want him noticing all of those things. You want first of all to use the technique—whether it is hand levitation, eye closure, relaxation.

Focusing Attention

Releasing Energy for Therapeutic Mental Activity
by Minimizing Irrelevant Movements

I treat a man with whatever technique it happens to be. You want him to give you his auditory attention. You also want him to give you his visual attention. You want him to give you his visual and auditory attention easily and comfortably—not because you say, "Now listen to me, now look at me." That isn't a nice way to speak to anybody. You ask a person to look at you by speaking to him in such a fashion that he is inclined to do it. You speak to him in such a fashion that he is inclined to listen to you, and so you fixate his visual attention; you fixate his auditory attention.

Then, what else do you do? It really isn't necessary that he do this, or this, or this, and that, and keep moving around and shifting his feet, and uncrossing his legs, and crossing them again, and fiddling with something in his pocket, and rapping the coins there, or examining to see if he brought along his airplane tickets, and let's see what else is there. No, you want the smallest amount of movement possible on the part of the patient, and you hold the patient's attention—visual and auditory. You are going to limit his movements. Every time you limit the patient's movements, you are then releasing for that patient energy for mental activity. Instead of thinking—*I'd better cross my legs now . . . Let's see . . . Shall I cross my right leg over my left one, or shall I cross my left one over my right one?*—you are getting him to think: *Let's see . . . That was about eight or nine years ago that happened to me, and I certainly didn't understand that particular thing.*

That is the thing you want the patient to do—to consider the matter that he came to see you about and not to debate if he should cross his legs or if he should shift his position in his chair. As he cuts down his movements, you discover that he is not smoothing his trouser legs or feeling the crease of the trousers; or she is not smoothing her dress, or anything of that sort. Her hands are still. Her breathing starts with a certain rhythm, and the patient is watching you and listening to you. The patient is thinking and going through mental activity, and so there is no need of taking a deep breath and sighing deeply. As the patient thinks this thing over, the patient is using mental images, memories, ideas, concepts, emotions of various sorts; and the patient is trying to understand that accumulated body of experience that is recorded in that patient's mind, and there is a free flowing of ideas that comes to the patient.

Minimal Cues of Emotional Complexes

Reading Faces, Hearing Intonations, Perceiving Breathing

The patient may be aware of all of those things; he may be aware of some of them. But you can watch that patient, and you can watch and notice what that patient's face is saying to you. You have a lifetime of experience in reading faces. You know very well when you tell a story to somebody, they listen to you so politely that you know they've heard that story before. Or you read the face and you know all they are thinking is, *Just as soon as he finishes telling that story, I've got a better one to tell him.* You read that on the face so easily and so comfortably.

You ought to be aware of the fact that you are doing that all the time in ordinary everyday life. You look at your patient in the same sort of an intelligent way and read his facial expression. You read the tone of his voice when he says something; you listen to those little intonations—the little hesitations. The breathing rhythm may be regular, but there may be a certain hesitation without disturbing the rhythm. And you ought to be aware of that, and you ought to make a mental note of that particular thing so that you can again bring up that particular item, and then again see if the patient shows a special alteration in their breathing or in their behavior of any kind. Then you are aware of the fact that here is the vital thing that ought to be handled carefully, and cautiously, and willingly.

> *Rossi:* From a psychoanalytic point of view we would say that the subtle alteration of breathing rhythms are minimal cues that an emotional complex (Jung's "feeling-toned complexes") has been activated. Such cues often gave Erickson the knowledge he needed to focus his hypnotherapeutic work precisely where it was needed, even if the patient did not know what the underlying problem was.

Facilitating Therapeutic Dreams Indirectly

Now, certainly you want the patient to fixate their attention visually and auditorially. You want to cut down their motor activity; you want to center all of their activity on the matters that are pertinent to the situation. You want the patient to have an open mind. By an open mind I mean not an open mind to believe anything and everything that you say, because I think you ought to be frank and free with your patient in telling your patient that there is a great deal that you really don't know. And it is true, you *don't* know a lot of things about your patient. In fact, the patient doesn't know a lot of things, but the patient may be able to recall a lot of things. You can point out to the patient the fact that things that you yourself haven't thought of for years—in a dream some night you may suddenly dream of that particular, long-forgotten thing.

Now, what have you told the patient? You have told the patient something that patient has known for a lifetime, because they have dreamed about the past. They have

12

dreamed about the past without being told to dream about the past, and you mention that,

> "Yes, there are a lot of things that I've forgotten, things that I've forgotten and don't even know that I have forgotten. Yet at nighttime, I can dream about those forgotten things. They come to my unconscious mind when I am sound asleep. They are very vivid, they are very real, very genuine, and they have an actuality based in fact."

Well, I'm no different than my patient. I don't have to tell the patient, "I am a human being, and you are a human being. If I can do this, so can you." Why should I tell the patient, "You can do the same thing." They are going to draw that conclusion themselves, and therefore you merely make mention of something and *let them finish—[let them] conclude your statement.* The two of you should be working *together,* and in working together, you can start a process and the other person is so very, very likely to complete it.

[Erickson apparently does an impromptu demonstration of securing cooperation by letting someone on stage finish what he started.] I didn't ask him to say a darn thing to me. All I did was to move a glass of water toward him, and he lifted his hands and he spoke to me. He made a perfectly natural, normal response to me stating, "That's yours," and he pointed to it, and I knew it was a glass of water. He didn't need to point to it, but he made it a very complete thing. *He participated, and he didn't realize that I was going to use him that easily and that quickly.* But what else could he do? He is a normal human being, and with a lifetime of experience in making responses, you ought to expect your patient to make responses whenever you offer them an opportunity.

> *Rossi:* Although this recording is incomplete, it nonetheless documents Erickson's utilization approach wherein he evokes a person's own "lifetime of experience in making responses." This utilization of a person's inner repertory of responses, rather than the

traditional reliance on the so-called "power of suggestion," is the essence of his hypnotherapeutic approach. This is best illustrated in a series of cases Erickson reported early in his career.[2]

Nonhypnotic and Hypnotic Amnesias

Utilizing Ordinary Conversation to Structure a
Blanket Amnesia; "Shifting Gears" and
"Letting the Patient Behave Normally"

There are a great wealth of hypnotic phenomena. *"What was that I just said to you?"* That's something that you hear in everyday life. Your wife starts to speak to you and you interrupt her with some irrelevant remark, and she replies to you, and then she says, "What was that I was going to say to you?" She has an amnesia for it. You ought to be aware of that fact in ordinary everyday life. And when you see a patient about to say something about something they ought not to say—because in your judgment, in your experience as a therapist, they really ought not to mention *that* thing just yet— I think you ought to be ready to interrupt them with something else so that you change their train of thought, their train of thinking, that train of association, so that that particular idea drops out of mind. Sooner or later that patient is going to have a recurrence. Not too often I find that people using hypnosis strive so desperately to get people to behavior normally, when all they need to do is to *let* the patient behave normally.

One of the questions so often asked is, "How can I induce a deep amnesia for a particular thing in a patient?" It is so easy to do that in ordinary everyday life. When I want a patient to develop a deep amnesia for a trance in my office, [I do the following]. As the patient comes in, I can remark to them so truthfully,

"It's such a nice clear day in Phoenix, Arizona—no fog, no smog, nothing of that sort. Just a nice clear, bright, sunny day."

14

I speak about the weather, and the patient comes in and sits down in the chair, and we have our therapeutic interview, and as the patient leaves I can remark:

"It is always a clear day in Arizona. The weather is always fine. I am hired by the Chamber of Commerce."

What have I done? All I have done is to *shift gears* for that patient—shifting gears so that the patient is back in the same mental gear as that in which the patient entered the office. So the patient enters the office with the foremost thought about the weather in Phoenix, the traffic on North Central, or some such thing far removed from the office; and when the patient leaves the office, the patient leaves with that same train of thought. I've said that remark about the traffic on North Central, or the weather, or the building up on North Central, or something of that sort, or the library, or the Heard Museum, or something of that sort. The patient thought I was just making conversation. Actually, I was saying a number of things, and then I would return to it all later. The patient would come into the office with a certain set of ideas and leave the office with the same set of ideas, so there would be a *blanket amnesia* for everything that occurred in the office.

Why should I tell the patient: "Now, I want you to forget everything that has taken place in the office"? Why not use the ordinary experience that the patient has had? And as you look over all hypnotic phenomena, you find that the patient will do that sort of thing. But you ought to be aware of it, and you ought to be willing to use it in that particular fashion.

Rossi: The dynamics of this "blanket amnesia" have been discussed as a "structured amnesia" in *Hypnotic Realities* and in *Hypnotherapy: An Exploratory Casebook*. This type of amnesia is very different from the "direct suggestion" for amnesia that is usually studied experimentally and may account, at least in part, for the differences in clinical and experimental hypnotic amnesia. Another major difference is the involvement of "state-dependent memory" in clinical situations, as discussed in the next section.[3]

Accessing Traumatic Amnesias

State-Dependent Memory: Forgetting "Year Things"
While Remembering "Brother Things"

This matter of the patient who says: "But I can't possibly remember any of the things that happened before my mother died, and I was 12 years old at the time, and [I] can't possibly remember." And I let the patient repeat that [sort of statement]. Now the patient is then convinced that I believe that fact. Why should I dispute the patient? If the patient wants to convince me of something, why shouldn't I let the patient convince me of that particular thing? I am well enough aware of human nature, human capabilities, to be aware that *people can do a lot of things of which they are unaware.* So if the patient wants me to believe, "I can't remember a thing previous to the twelfth year of my life," I'll take their word for it; and then I will let them tell me again, and maybe a second, a third, and a fourth time. I will let them tell me in slightly different ways, so that they have an intense feeling of conviction that I really do honestly and completely believe they can't remember a solitary thing previous to their twelfth year of life.

Then somehow or other I happen to ask about their brother, who happens to be older than they are. Now that is a perfectly acceptable thing to talk about. The brother who is older than [the patient], therefore, when the patient was 12—that brother was older than 12; therefore, that brother existed after the age of 12. But, you know, *brother* has other associations; and if there is a younger brother, then I bridge the gap to remembering a younger brother.

Now, the younger brother has certain associations. Let us say that the patient is a girl—a woman. Certainly every girl has certain memories of her younger brother who was such a pest and such a nuisance, and so she *is* going to remember certain "brother things." She has told me she can't remember certain

16

"year things," but she is going to tell me certain "brother things"—so I let her tell me about certain "brother things." I have broken the barrier of the years, and I have broken through that rigid, false belief of hers that she can't remember anything previous to her twelfth year of life. She has just talked about her younger brother, and she is not thinking: *He is four years younger than I am; therefore, when I was 12, he was eight years old, and a pain in the neck to me, and a thorough-going pain in the neck to me.*

She is going to tell me about that younger brother with a wealth of memory, and that is all she is talking about. She thinks she isn't talking about memories previous to the twelfth year of her life [but obviously she is, if she talks about the brother when he was eight or younger]. But there are too many people who take a dogmatic statement of that sort as a valid utterance when it isn't a valid utterance.

I think you ought to be aware of the fact that you should give your patient whatever sense of comfort that they demand. If they demand that they should sit in an upright chair with a hardwood seat and tell you that is comfortable, I don't think that you ought to enter into an argument with them [about another] nice, comfortable chair [that] is much more comfortable. They didn't come there to argue with you about the chair. They came there for certain other purposes. They didn't come there to argue with you about whether they remembered things previous to their twelfth year of life or not, but you ought to be aware of the fact that, unquestionably, they do remember things. But please don't ask them to label those memories as previous to the twelfth year! Let them label those memories much more correctly in terms of younger brother, in terms of younger sister, in terms of their street address, in terms of the city in which they lived.

Rossi: We now know that memories associated with stress and trauma are encoded as "state-dependent memories" by the stress hormones (ACTH, epinephrine, B-endorphin, etc.) that are evoked by Selye's General Adaptation Syndrome.[4] These memories are often arranged in different "files"[5] so that patients can speak the truth of their experience when they say, in effect, "My memory file labeled *Before Age 12* is empty." Yet such memories can be available under another file name such as *Memories of My Pain-in-the-Neck Younger Brother*. The practical work of the hypnotherapist often involves accessing these traumatic memories by searching for their "correct file name" without allowing a "blocking file name" to interfere. Izquierdo (1989) discusses the experimental evidence supporting the view that even amnesias due to electroshock treatment have a state-dependent component, so that they can often be recovered by a procedure such as Erickson discusses in the next section.

Circumventing Traumatic Amnesias

Accessing State-Dependent Memory (Amnesia)
Due to Electroshock Treatments: Utilizing the
Longitudinal History of the Patient: "Zed"!

I can think of a patient who came to me and said: "I had 30 electric shocks, and it has knocked out every bit of memory that I've had ever since I've grown up. I don't remember a solitary thing that has happened to me previous to my twentieth year of life. All I can remember is that I was married, and I don't know whether I was married at 18 or 17 or 19. All I can remember is that I was married at 20. That is what the electric shocks did to me. It disturbed my memory completely, and I've lost all my memories."

I sympathized with the patient about that loss of memories and then I commented on the fact: "You know, do you mind repeating the alphabet to me? I think it would be very interesting. It is an odd request for me to make of you, to repeat the alphabet, but I really would like to have you do it."

The patient said: "I don't mind doing it [even though] it seems silly: *A, B, C, D, E, F, G, H, I, J, K, L, M, N, O, P, Q, R, S, T, U, V, W, X, Y, Zed.*"

How did *zed* get into there? The patient shouldn't have said *zed,* but I had noticed an English accent. As I listened to that accent, I wondered what part of Canada [she was from], and then the next question I asked was: "In going to school, what form did you reach?" That was an old, familiar question; I wasn't disputing that she had no memories since the age of 20. And she said that she went up to such-and-such form at Port Arthur. I said, "I don't remember where Port Arthur is," so she promptly gave me the location of Port Arthur. The first thing we knew, we were involved in an extensive discussion of childhood memories!

But that vocabulary—that recitation of vocabulary looked like such a stupid and innocent and useless and worthless thing to do, and the patient didn't mind doing it. But I knew that there was a likelihood from my Canadian friends for her to say *zed* instead of *zee.* Well, let her say *zed.* Once she said *zed,* I'd have a wide open door for asking a lot of other things that related to, let's say, Canada, or to England—something that would not be related to the United States. Before the therapeutic sessions were over, the patient spoke to me in great length about the remarkable ease with which I had restored a lot of her lost memories. But I think she had some rather set ideas about her memories being lost. I think she had them but that her antagonism, her resentment, toward the shock therapy made her exclude those memories so that she could continue resenting the previous psychiatric therapy she had received.

I think all of you ought to recognize that when you want to use hypnosis, you [need to] use hypnotic techniques to fixate attention—visual, auditory, and physical attention (holding the head still, the face still, and the body still). Then you want to make use of other normal phenomena of everyday life such as amnesia, and then such as unexpected memories that relate not only to the immediate present but relate to past learnings— past learnings of yesterday, and yesteryear, and of a decade ago, and 20 years ago, and longer ago.

These are the things that you ought to be interested in: your patient as a complete object [who has a] longitudinal history as well as a horizontal history. You see the patient in a certain relationship, but you had better bear in mind that that patient has a long, long history that reaches far back. The five-year-old child [has a] five-year-old history that reaches way back (five years is a lifetime to a child), and you'd better respect the five years as [constituting] as much of a lifetime to the five-year-old child as 90 years is to a 90-year-old—because it *is* a lifetime.

Making Use of Everyday Amnesias and Dissociations for Anesthesia

Utilizing a Patient's Interests to Distract and Fixate Attention in Emergency Surgery and Cesarean Section; Bifurcating Voice Tone and Surgical Hand Movements

Now these amnesias, these hypermnesias, are awfully important considerations in dealing with patients. In this matter of dissociation, it is a rather easy thing to forget where you are in ordinary everyday life. You can be reading a suspense story and forget all about a lot of things. You can go to a suspense movie, and to make yourself comfortable (if you happen to wear dresses), you kick off your shoes to be comfortable while you look at the suspense movie. And then you start to walk out and suddenly remember, "Oh, where are my shoes?" Then you start scrambling around trying to find your shoes. You haven't been thinking about those shoes for a long, long time. Where have you been? You have been up there on the screen, perhaps participating.

Haven't you ever been in a movie theater where somebody in the audience suddenly yelled, "Look out!" to the hero. That hero was very, very real, and they forgot they were sitting in an audience, that it was a movie, and that there was an audience. And having yelled, "Look out!", they feel terribly embarrassed, because they have a totally different sort of a situation.

That matter of dissociation is a very common thing. I think that in the therapeutic situation—whether it is a dental one or a psychological situation, a psychiatric one, [or] whether it is a general practitioner's office—you ought to be willing to

20

make use of dissociation as a very common thing, and you make use of dissociation in a wealth of ways. How can you make use of dissociation in a wealth of ways?

The general practitioner says to his patient: "We have a serious laceration of the hand." It is resting on the surgical table and the general practitioner says:

> "You notice that picture of the wheat field over there. How many different ways can you tell me exactly how that is a wheat field? I think it is a good painting, and it really is a good painting, but how did the artist really capture the appearance of a wheat field? Wheat bends in a certain way in the wind; wheat carries a certain visual quality as you look at it. And as you study that picture, how near ripe is the wheat? How near is it to harvest time? What do you really think about that wheat? Was it sown too heavily, too thickly? Was the soil properly fertilized? Is it poor soil?"

As the farmer studies the wheat field, the general practitioner ought to be rather busy putting the sutures in that arm. He has got his patient dissociated and recalling every one of his memories, ideas, and concepts of what a wheat field really looks like—how one senses wheat, and really studying that particular thing. As the farmer studies it, the general practitioner can handle that injured hand very nicely, very gently; and he is still running off at the mouth about those questions about the wheat field!

I think all of you ought to see Ralph August's picture made by UpJohn about a Cesarean operation under hypnosis— hypnosis being the only anesthetic. Ralph August, as he does the Cesarean there, is talking to the patient, and he is doing very careful surgical work. And as you listen to Ralph August in the movie, you literally feel his presence. You hear his voice. You know if you watch and listen to him with a very critical ear, that he is talking somewhat automatically, that he has made up his mind [that] he is going to say things that are going to be of interest to his patient. In other words, he has a wide acquaintance with the ideas of interest to his patient. But he also has a wide acquaintance with surgery, and he is well aware of the fact that one can talk very easily and very comfortably while one is really giving his attention to exactly taking hold of this particular bit of tissue and attaching it to that particular piece of tissue.

Yet all the time Ralph August was talking to the patient, it was [with] one tone of voice. And if you watched his hands, there was another tonus of movement that was not in accord with the tonus of the organs of speech. It is a very delightful film to watch, and it is an extremely instructive one to watch. I hope every one of you will watch that film and note the difference between August's tone of voice in the way he talks to the patient, and the appropriateness of the things that he says, and the totally different rhythm of his hand movements, and the way he reaches for something and the way he takes hold of something while he is asking the patient:

"Would you like to sing now? And what would you like to sing about? Are things going well? How do you feel?"

There are two levels of conversation that Ralph August carries on with that patient, and does so very nicely; and when he speaks to an assistant of his, there is a third tone of voice that comes into play. Now, that film was done very, very nicely. Upjohn and Company produced it about a year ago and have shown it to about 40,000 physicians upon request. It is one they like to loan out to companies, to any medical group, and it is worth anybody's attention to see that film. I'm pretty certain that if this group were to write, Upjohn and Company would be very glad to let you see it.

Multiple Levels of Behavior

*The Use of Distraction to Provide Ultradian
"Rest" from Traumatic Memories*

Now, when you work with a patient, you'd better be aware

22

of the fact that there are a lot of things that you can do at different levels of behavior. You can be walking down the street and be discussing mathematical theory. I can't think of anything more abstruse and more uninteresting than mathematical theory. It's utterly abstract, and it's painful to listen to. I know [because] I have a son who likes to talk it, but he can talk it in the most happy and delightful fashion, and suddenly stop and say, "I have got to tie my shoestring." Now, his shoestring did not come untied at that particular moment; he was interested in discussing mathematical theory. At the right moment his unconscious mind nudged his conscious mind and said: *Listen, Bud, your shoestring is untied.* And so he interrupted his mathematical discussion, and [he] tied his shoestring, and then resumed his mathematical discussion, and went right along with no particular interruption.

Now, that is ordinary everyday life. I think you ought to recognize that your patient in the office can do precisely and exactly the same sort of thing. Whenever you see a patient getting tired, getting a little bit tense, I think you ought to distract their attention with something like this. Ask them what they think of that paperweight, and then give them an uninteresting discussion of what a thunderegg is, and how certain silicate salts seep in and form agate. And they listen to you attentively. What they don't know is that you are giving them *a rest from some rather traumatic emotional memories* that you have aroused and that they themselves assist in arousing, and therefore you ought to give them an opportunity to build up their strength to face those particular things. I think that one serious fault in therapy is this tendency to drive home, and stick to the last, and hammer away as if your patient should be given every possible second of your therapeutic time. They *do* need to pause, and to take a breath, and you'd better recognize that they take the pause and they take the breath for *their* benefit, not yours.

Rossi: I am not aware of anyone else talking about the significance of fatigue in psychotherapy back in 1964 when Erickson spoke these words. I believe, however, that this is an example of how Erickson recognized the relevance of the rest phase of our 90-minute ultradian rhythms in therapy. He would often use these periods to facilitate a therapeutic trance. His belief that patients are taking "a rest from some rather traumatic emotional memories" supports the hypothesis that unconscious processes are more available during these natural ultradian rest periods.[6]

Depersonalization, Dissociation and Projection

Utilizing Everyday Dissociations to Avoid Accusation and Facilitate Receptivity to New Understandings: Henry's Disembodied Intellect

Now, another thing that one notices—and you notice it in the little child in particular, and little children do that so beautifully, and I think you ought to observe it very, very carefully—and that is this matter of depersonalization. Depersonalization is a tremendously important hypnotic phenomenon wherein the person drops his own identity as a self and becomes another identity.

The little child comes to you and says, "My finger—it hurts!" *My finger* identifies *it,* and then the child talks about its finger hurting, and the child disclaims the hurt and accuses the finger of doing the hurting!

I think that you'd better recognize that that goes on throughout life. We *all* do it, no matter what age we reach. We do tend to anthropomorphize the various parts of our body— to treat them as objects separate from our own personal identity.

"I'm all right. It's only my heart that is getting old."

"I'm all right. It is only my joints that are bothering me."

There are a lot of things that people say to you. *They're* all right—it's this particular part that is not doing the right thing.

So you ask the patient in an hypnotic situation (undergoing hypnotic therapy) to employ this phenomenon of dissociation of a part. It is so much easier to talk about a dissociated part, and how far does that dissociation go?

"Now, when I was a young man, I did things differently."

[In other words,] that isn't what *I* would do [now]—that is what a youngster would do. [There you have] the dissociation of the self. So you talk about that *youngster* and the way that *youngster* used to behave. So you ask [the patient] to dissociate, and he can talk much more freely about that youngster of years ago than he can talk about *himself* behaving that way years ago. You are asking him now, today, to accept the responsibility of that irresponsible kid of 40 years ago, and he doesn't want to accept the responsibility of that kid of 40 years ago. He is willing to accept his responsibilities today as a successful businessman, but he doesn't want to accept the responsibilities of that person of 40 years ago.

You'd better be willing to accept that matter of dissociation—this matter of utilizing dissociation. It's common in everyday life. As you listen to your patient carefully, you ought to listen for that dissociation in their voice, their dissociation of this or that particular thing. What does that dissociation tell you? It tells you exactly how they may feel about that particular incident. And I'd much rather ask a patient about what *that boy* did in college than I would : "What did *you* do in college?" What did *that boy* do, and what did *that boy's* father think about it? What did *that boy's* mother do about it? And what was the attitude of *those* parents? I'm certainly not going to ask him, "What did *your* parents think, and how do *you* feel about what *you* did," because I am accusing him.

Now, is it my job to accuse him? Any mention of something that he finds displeasing is going to be something that my mention of will sound like an accusation. But when I start talking about *those parents*, we are talking about a *topic*—a subject—about *those parents*. We're not naming the identity. We are depersonalizing them and that particular boy. How did he really feel? I'm not asking my patient to accept a personal responsibility, and therefore he does not feel that I am accusing him, that I'm passing emotional judgment on him. I am simply using the natural process of depersonalization so that he can discuss it in a depersonalized manner.

I am thinking of the article I published in the early 1940s where a man named Henry just simply could not talk to me about the quarrel he had with his wife and his mother-in-law.7 Therefore, what did I do with Henry? He was in a very nice deep trance, and so I asked Henry to lose all of his identity as a person. But I asked him to be a highly intelligent mind, and I asked this highly intelligent mind to look at that movie back there. It was a rather interesting movie.

"You know, there are three people in that movie.
It is an odd way they are behaving."

And this depersonalized, disembodied intellect agreed with me. He was simply an intellectual voice, and so this identity-less intelligence described "that man there and that woman there, and that other woman there who seems to be the mother of the first woman, and that man seems to be that second woman's son-in-law. Isn't it disgraceful the way they are quarreling in the department store? Even the clerk is looking on."

And it was a very delightful discussion. Certainly that man did not want to tell me about *his own* disgraceful behavior, so I simply used the depersonalization. I used the phenomenon of projection, too. The man himself had repressed it. He didn't want to think about it and he had repressed it. So why should I ask him to give up his own defenses against those particular memories? So I asked him to be just a highly intelligent voice and discuss with me a movie—which was no more than a projection that came out from underneath his suppressions and repressions and became visible on that movie screen. We had an utterly delightful time going over the behavior of those three people who didn't know they were under observation. I got a very adequate understanding, and I could make some intelligent comments, and I could point out where that man was at fault, where both women were at fault. I could point out where each of the people could have been understood better.

This intelligent voice sitting beside me, looking on at the movie, could agree or disagree, but he could evaluate it at an intellectual level entirely. And in evaluating it at an intellectual level entirely, he opened his mind to other possible understandings. We all know that when we have got certain emotional feelings about certain things, that we are not going to be very open-minded on the reasonableness of the other person's attitude, behavior, conduct, or remarks. For example, all of my remarks on the subject of Arizona and water, I certainly do not expect to be believed by this audience. Now let's have some coffee.

> *Rossi:* In this section Erickson is referring to his important paper, "Hypnotic Psychotherapy." In this early paper published in 1948, he outlines the essence of his innovative "indirect utilization" approach to the "*neuro-psycho-physiological*" process of suggestion. Since this approach has been so often misunderstood by critics, researchers, and clinicians alike, it may be well to quote the section on the "Role of Suggestion in Hypnosis" in its entirety and discuss how its meaning has been grossly distorted by recent research:
>
> "The next consideration concerns the general role of suggestion in hypnosis. Too often the unwarranted and unsound assumption is made that, since a trance state is induced and maintained by suggestion, and since hypnotic manifestations can be elicited by suggestion, whatever develops from hypnosis must necessarily be completely a result of suggestion and primarily an expression of it.
>
> "Contrary to such misconceptions, the hypnotized person remains the same person. His or her behavior only is altered by the trance state, but even so, that altered behavior derives from the life experience of the patient and not from the therapist. At the most the therapist can influence only the manner of self-expression. The induction and maintenance of a trance serve to provide a special psychological state in which patients can reassociate and reorganize their inner psychological complexities and utilize their own capacities in a manner in accord with their own experiential life. Hypnosis does not change people nor does

it alter their past experiential life. It serves to permit them to learn more about themselves and to express themselves more adequately.

"Direct suggestion is based primarily, if unwittingly, upon the assumption that whatever develops in hypnosis derives from the suggestions given. It implies that the therapist has the miraculous power of effecting therapeutic changes in the patient, and disregards the fact that therapy results from an inner resynthesis of the patient's behavior achieved by the patient himself. It is true that direct suggestion can effect an alteration in the patient's behavior and result in a symptomatic cure, at least temporarily. However, such a "cure" is simply a response to the suggestion and does not entail that reassociation and reorganization of ideas, understandings, and memories so essential for an actual cure. It is this experience of reassociating and reorganizing his own experiential life that eventuates in a cure, not the manifestation of responsive behavior which can, at best, satisfy only the observer.

"For example, anesthesia of the hand may be suggested directly, and a seemingly adequate response may be made. However, if the patient has not spontaneously interpreted the command to include a realization of the need for inner reorganization, that anesthesia will fail to meet clinical tests and will be a pseudo-anesthesia.

"An effective anesthesia is better induced, for example, by initiating a train of mental activity within the patient himself by suggesting that he recall the feeling of numbness experienced after a local anesthetic, or after a leg or arm went to sleep, and then suggesting that he can now experience a similar feeling in his hand. By such an indirect suggestion the patient is enabled to go through those difficult inner processes of disorganizing, reorganizing, reassociating, and projecting of inner real experience to meet the requirements of the suggestion, and thus the induced anesthesia becomes a part of his experiential life instead of a simple superficial response.

"The same principles hold true in psychotherapy. The chronic alcoholic can be induced by direct suggestion to correct his habits temporarily, but not until he goes through the inner process of reassociating and reorganizing his experiential life can effective results occur.

"In other words, hypnotic psychotherapy is a learning process for the patient, a procedure of re-education. Effective results in hypnotic psychotherapy, or hypnotherapy, derive only from the patient's activities. The therapist merely stimulates the patient into activity, often not knowing what that activity may be, and then guides the patient and exercises clinical judgment in determining the amount of work to be done to achieve the desired results. How to guide and to judge constitute the therapist's problem, while the patient's task is that of learning through his own efforts to understand his experiential life in a new way. Such reeducation is, of course, necessarily in terms of the patient's life experiences, his understandings, memories, attitudes, and ideas; it cannot be in terms of the therapist's ideas and opinions. For example, in training a gravid patient to develop anesthesia for eventual delivery, use was made of the suggestions outlined above as suitable. The attempt failed completely even though she had previously experienced local dental anesthesia and also her legs "going to sleep." Accordingly, the suggestion was offered that she might develop a generalized anesthesia in terms of her own experiences when her body was without sensory meaning to her. This suggestion was intentionally vague since the patient, knowing the purpose of the hypnosis, was enabled by the vagueness of the suggestion to make her own selection of those items of personal experience that would best enable her to act upon the suggestion.

"She responded by reviewing mentally the absence of any memories of physical stimuli during physiological sleep, and by reviewing her dreams of walking effortlessly and without sensation through closed doors and walls and floating pleasantly through the air as a disembodied spirit looking happily down upon her sleeping, unfeeling body. By means of this review she was able to initiate a process of reorganization of her experiential life. As a result she was able to develop a remarkably effective anesthesia which met fully the needs of the subsequent delivery. Not until sometime later did the therapist learn by what train of thought he had initiated the neuro-psycho-physiological processes by which she achieved anesthesia." (pp. 38-39)

These words, published more than 40 years ago, still challenge us with their implications. The general public and most professionals still cling to a primitive view of suggestion as a way of programming and forcing behavioral compliance on a hypnotized subject, who erroneously is believed to be defenseless and automaton-like in trance. The recent flurry of studies by academic researchers purporting to investigate the effectiveness of "indirect suggestion," for example, completely misunderstand Erickson's view as expressed above:

"By such indirect suggestion, the patient is enabled to go through those difficult inner processes of disorganizing, reorganizing, reassociating, and projecting of inner real experience . . . instead of a simple superficial response."

Most of the studies that purport to have found that indirect suggestion is not as effective as direct suggestion measured what Erickson would call "simple, superficial responses."[8] It is a caricature of Erickson's view of indirect suggestion as a "difficult inner process of disorganizing, reorganizing, and reassociating" *meaningful and highly motivating personal psychodynamics* to claim, as do Stone and Lundy, that they have found no difference in direct and indirect suggestion when they compare the following "simple, superficial responses":

Indirect Suggestion	**Direct Suggestion**
"Your eyes *can* open now, and then close again."	"Your eyes *will* open now, and then close again."

This ingenious misunderstanding would not even require comment except for the fact that such superficial studies are published with all the paraphernalia of sound statistical analysis in our leading scientific journals—and worse, claim to have won the day in proving the case against the effectiveness of Erickson's indirect approach.

The truth is, no one has yet published an objective assessment of *Erickson's view* of indirect suggestion. Even clinicians who have developed "indirect scales of suggestion" in hopes of utilizing Erickson's approach[9] rarely, if ever, engage the subject's personal dynamics in meaningful and highly motivating conditions, as Erickson describes in virtually all of his case histories in which he illustrates his *indirect* utilization approach. This engagement and utilization of personal, motivational psychodynamics in real-life circumstances is the major difference between research in academic settings and the clinical situations of the typical practitioner; the absence of it remains as the major stumbling block in establishing a sound science of hypnotherapy. The current development of *single case research designs* by Kazdin, particularly as used by Nugent, may be a way of integrating the scientific and clinical approaches to hypnotherapy.[10]

Comparing Hypnosis and Psychoanalysis

Freud's Preference for Free Association;
No "One Way" for All Patients; Hypnosis Applies to
"Every Expression of Human Behavior"

This was a question that was raised to me: that I should compare hypnosis with psychoanalysis. Actually, of course, what I would like to say is this: Psychoanalysis is a very valuable therapy. Freud was first interested in neurology; he contributed extensively to the field of neurology. He was the man who developed the use of cocaine as a local anesthetic. He did some of the neurological studies in locating a certain petromizone—I can't say the rest of the name—a peculiar kind of fish, a neuronic cell, that turned out to be a ganglionic cell. It belongs to the [inaudible] family. It was a very remarkable study, and he should receive a great deal of credit for that particular piece of work.

In 1888 Freud become interested in hypnosis and he used it extensively. Freud, however, was rather timid in many ways, and he made no pretense of not being timid, and he did not like to touch patients, and he liked to avoid it. He studied under Janet and Bernheim, and stroking of the forehead and various forms of physical contact were employed to induce hypnosis. Freud found that repulsive to him. He didn't like to touch patients, and so he disliked that particular bit of teaching. Freud didn't recognize that touching patients isn't really an essential part of inducing hypnosis. Freud used hypnosis for about 18 years—8 years—[until] 1896, and then Freud discovered that he could not use it for all patients. Therefore, he decided that he ought to find some method he could use for *all* patients. Well, that was a perfectly good idea in the early days of the development of psychiatry, but one way for *all* patients is a rather naive thing. But it is not to Freud's discredit that he felt that way.

[Freud] found out that he had much more interest in free association than he had in hypnosis. Freud's feeling was that he was much better equipped to ride one horse [in] one direction than two horses in two directions. So he dropped hypnosis and took up free association, and he contributed very extensively to the field of psychiatry, and [he] developed some very valuable concepts. But Freud himself was not under the illusion that he had discovered the *only* possible way of handling psychiatric problems, which was a mistaken idea that some of his students have had.

Now, in relationship to hypnosis and psychoanalysis, I think the difference between hypnosis and psychoanalysis is this: that hypnosis is something that deals with human behavior—human behavior in the ordinary waking state, human behavior in various particular situations. Psychoanalysis tends to depend upon a certain setting. One can use hypnosis in the psychoanalytic setting, one can use it in the Adlerian setting, one can use hypnosis in the Rogerian, the Stiechelian, the Myerian, or whatever field of psychoanalytic thought or psychiatric thought or school of interpretative psychology and psychiatry there is. *Hypnosis deals essentially with human behavior,* and in every school of thought, you are dealing with human behavior. So hypnosis is not limited just to the field of hypnosis, but it applies to every expression of human behavior regardless of the general field of thought in which you want to include hypnosis.

The Logic and Illogic of Therapy for Psychosis

Accepting Illogical Ideas (Hallucinations) as Real: "Those Nude Young Men up There"; Temporary Weekend Psychoses

Now, I have been asked to discuss this matter of logic versus illogic. One of the things that troubles the average therapist is this: that he likes to be logical with his patients. His patients come to him with various illogical ideas, and your first intention is to correct that illogical idea. I think that is awfully wrong, because if your patient comes to you with enough faith in you to believe that you are going to accept those illogical ideas, you have an opening with that patient, and I think you ought to respect it.

33

I can think of the 30-year-old girl who came to me and said: "I need psychotherapy, and I need it badly. But I don't know whether you are the right psychotherapist for me. But I need it, and I wonder if you are going to do the same thing that a lot of other psychiatrists have done."

I said:

"Well, I hope I don't make any mistakes. I'll just try to do the right sort of thing, and at least I'll try. I won't guarantee that I'll do the right sort of thing."

She said: "My trouble is this. I get along all right in the world. I adjust satisfactorily. Nobody knows that there is anything wrong with me. I don't let them find it out, but it troubles me very, very much to have those nude young men up there following me down the street!"

There was a whole flock of nude young men right up there who were following her everywhere! And I said:

"Well, so far as I can see, they are not really trying to disturb you. Perhaps you and I can discuss them, and discuss other matters, while they remain quiet up there."

Then she happened to notice over in the corner of my office that I happened to have half a dozen nude dancing girls! And she asked me if I thought that was a right and ethical thing for a psychiatrist to have in his office—nude dancing girls.

I said that, well, it's a question of man's ethics belonging to the victim himself, and that as long as those nude dancing girls behaved themselves, and didn't fraternize with her nude young men up there, that I thought things would get along all right. I was pretty sure that those dancing girls would behave themselves and remain in that alcove in my office. And, you know, they did!

Then the question came: What can we do about those nude young men who followed her down the street and troubled her? They entered every building with her and hovered over her head, embarrassing as can be. And the question came up,

"Well, what should we do with them? There ought to be some place you ought to dispose of them."

Now, [if] any of you are interested in seeing those nude young men—she and I agreed that we could put them in the closet in my office, and they are still there! She came back five years later to see if they were in good condition, and they were! In the meantime, she has taught school successfully. She has been the private secretary of a nationally known president of a nationally known firm. She is rather a successful person.

Periodically, she writes me a letter in which she says, "Under separate cover, I am sending you another fragment of my psychosis." In a manilla envelope there will be some torn pieces of the paper, some pictures of some utterly illogical things—completely illogical, unreasonable. Those are her temporary psychoses of the weekend, because we agreed whenever she wanted to have a psychosis, a weekend would be an awfully good time to have it. It wouldn't interfere with work. Nobody would notice it; she could enjoy it quietly, privately, in the privacy of her own apartment. It would be a good idea to stock up on food, because there was no use in starving the body while her psychosis was visiting with her. And when she was through with it on Monday morning, she ought to put it in an envelope and mail it to me.

She has checked my file to see if I kept those psychotic episodes. Well, of course, I have kept the psychotic episodes. I have a whole drawer full of them, and if you want to have some them, you are welcome to them. But I don't think you can use them, because they fit *her*. But so far as the world is concerned, she is a well-adjusted person, and she still wonders whatever did happen to those nude dancing girls I had in the alcove!

There is one other thing that troubled her. She didn't think I was quite an ethical psychiatrist because what she couldn't understand was that great big steel bear trap that was set right in the middle of the floor, so that an incautious patient might step on it and be caught and be held in my office. And she always walked around it. I incautiously went to the door and almost stepped into it. She leaped out [of her chair and] knocked me to one side so I wouldn't step in that bear trap, because it was very, very real [to her]. So, thereafter, I walked around it and so did she, until finally we agreed that it would be all right if I threw that bear trap out into the alley, after first carefully springing it and thus rendering it harmless.

Why should I ever tell that psychotic woman that that bear trap was a hallucination? Why should I tell her that those nude dancing girls were definitely a hallucination? That the nude young men were hallucinations? They were *real* to her. They were a part of her life, so I accepted that which was real to her.

The woman who tells me that her husband loves her and she believes it implicitly, and I know enough about the family to know that her husband does not love her: I'm simply not going to enter into an argument with her. I'll take her word for it until she is in a position to understand whether or not her husband loves her. And the same with her husband. You've got exactly the same sort of illogic there.

Depotentiating the Illogic of Self-Derogation

Reciprocal Freedom to Reject and Accept;
Presenting a Fragmentation of Ideas for
Gradual Assimilation

The patient who comes in and says, "I am hideous . . . nobody can possibly like me . . . I am inferior . . . I am undesirable . . . I am unlikable"—well, why dispute this? And so I want to know all the different ways in which they *are* unlikable.

> "Is it your hairline that is unlikable? Or do you really have a nice hairline? To me, that widow's peak you've got looks awfully good to me, but then you might not like the widow's peak—that might be just my personal liking."

She'll have to admit that it might be my personal liking, but what she doesn't realize is that she has admitted unwittingly that a widow's peak can be likable. I haven't asked *her* to like *her* widow's peak, but she has to give you the same freedom

36

to like it as she has freedom to dislike it. And so, one by one, you go through her features. And if she wants to discredit her eyebrows, that is perfectly all right; and she can discredit any feature that she has got. But I'm pretty certain that I can find something about a feature here or there that in some peculiar way, in my own odd sort of way, that I like. And I give her the freedom to *dislike* it and she gives me the freedom to *like* it. But when she gives me the freedom to like it, she is also breaking down the illogic of her own self-derogation, because she is admitting that at least one person in this world can like a particular thing.

[*End of audiotape*]

Manipulation in Hypnosis

Manipulation in Medical and Dental Settings; the Ethics of Facilitating the Patient's Welfare by "Doing the Things That Are Feasible and Reasonable"

. . . .This afternoon I was asked to make a comment concerning this matter of *manipulation*, not only from the psychoanalytical point of view but also from the point of view of other schools of psychiatric thought.

In hypnosis one does manipulate the patient, but as I understand it, only in the manner that one manipulates the patient in surgery; only in the manner that I understand how one manipulates the patient in dentistry. In practically every field of the healing arts, you manipulate the patient. But I think that *manipulation should be in accord with the patient's own welfare.*

I am going to give you one example in which a group of psychoanalysts decided to take me before the Board of Ethics of the Wayne County Medical Society.

A psychoanalyst had a patient in therapy. For three months, the patient had been resisting. The patient had gone for sessions one hour each day, for six to eight weeks, and had proceeded to lie down on the couch and read *Time Magazine* or some current book. Each time, this behavior was interpreted by the psychoanalyst as being resistant. Yet the patient felt completely unable to do anything at all about that resisting behavior.

Finally in late August the patient came to me and explained, "This is what I am doing, and I can't get out of it at all."

My statement was simply this: "Listen, Jean. You have been a hypnotic subject of mine. (She had worked for me as a subject previous to her psychoanalysis; I had kept my hands off her when she went into psychoanalysis).

"Suppose you go into a trance right now and tell me the whole thing again, as if I didn't know anything at all about it."

Jean went into a trance and told me all about her resistant behavior. Then I told her,

"In your next psychoanalytic situation, why don't you surprise the living daylights out of your analyst by pouring out all the information you have withheld from him for three long months, and deluge him with it?"

At the next meeting, to her analyst's surprise, she really deluged him with the information she had been withholding. When he asked her how she had overcome that resistance, she answered very simply: "I was running out of funds to pay you, so I asked my friend, Dr. Erickson, to interfere and put an end to my resistance."

I manipulated her, and so her psychoanalyst took it up with the Ethics Board to see whether or not I should be disciplined for interfering with another physician's patient. My statement to them was rather harsh and unkind. I said that I did not agree with the ethics of any person who would manipulate a patient for three long months for so many dollars per hour, and that I wanted to hear no more about any complaints. I had done something for free that had helped the patient. That ended that inquiry into my ethics!

Now, in hypnosis, patients come to you for aid; they cannot

handle their problem. I think you ought to be willing to help them to handle it, even if it does mean picking them up and putting them down in another chair; even if it does mean manipulating them so that they face East instead of West! Part of therapy is manipulating the patient's thinking and feeling and attitude and behavior *so that he can do the things that are feasible and reasonable for him.*

I think it is an utterly unjust denunciation of hypnosis or of the use of hypnosis to say that it is manipulative. I think that is the attitude of the person who wants to attach a term of derogation without thinking things through, without any desire to be honest or thoughtful or considerate of the values intended, of the very real values that exist. There are so many people who like to attach derogatory terms to something that they do not understand.

> *Rossi*: This is a particularly instructive example of what Erickson meant by "manipulation." In trance he first has the woman review her "resistant" behavior. She is actually being asked to access and experience her "resistance." Once the reality of her resistance is being experienced, Erickson then helps her utilize it in a creative and therapeutic way with the question, "In your next psychoanalytic session, why don't you *surprise the living daylights* out of your analyst by pouring out all the information you have withheld from him for three long months, and *deluge* him with it?"
>
> Perhaps Erickson surmised that her so-called resistance was some form of power struggle—perhaps an indirect manifestation of aggression or hostility. By asking her to "surprise" and "deluge" her analyst with the information she had withheld, Erickson is helping her express her power and/or aggression in a more effective way. This is a naturalistic and utilization approach: it utilizes what is naturally within the patient for the patient's own benefit and learning.
>
> This is not "manipulation" in the conventional sense of imposing something foreign on a person and

managing their behavior in favor of the manipulator! Erickson emphasizes that manipulation is used to help a patient "so that he can do the things that are feasible and reasonable for him." It certainly requires some wisdom to recognize what is of real and reasonable value to the patient from the patient's own point of view, rather than the therapist projecting his own views and needs upon the patient. Many detailed examples of Erickson's naturalistic and utilization approaches to so-called manipulation can be found in Volume I of Erickson's *Collected Papers* (pp. 168-176). A more formal treatment of this issue is presented in the final section of this book, "Creative Choice in Therapeutic Hypnosis."

Time Distortion in Hypnosis

The Subjective Nature of One's Sense of Time: "Comfortable" Vs. "Disagreeable" Time; Variations in Length of Time for Trance Induction Similar to Sleep Patterns

. . . . One uses hypnosis not only to enable patients to understand their problems but also to develop enough strength to *handle* their problems. A patient will tell you: "I can stand so many things for a certain length of time, and then my strength and my courage give out." But suppose you can teach that patient something about subjective time values. Old friends can come and visit you and stay all afternoon, and at six o'clock you wonder, *Where on earth did the afternoon go?* If you try to hold your breath just a full 60 seconds, however, you wonder if that second hand on the stopwatch has stopped moving, because 60 seconds is so very, very long to hold your breath. Try it some time. Try to hold your breath for two minutes. Then you will really know what a long period of time is.

So in the matter of handling a patient who says he has unbearable problems that he can endure only a certain length of time, you distort time for him. You make his subjective sense of time different so that comfortable time is expanded and lasts and lasts and lasts, while disagreeable time is experienced as very, very brief.

One does that in the case of the arthritic patient who has intolerable pain; one does that with the cancer patient who is suffering intolerable pain. You tell that patient with the intolerable pain:

> "You do have some periods where you are pain-free. Let those periods of freedom from pain get longer and longer until they seem to last all day."

You are manipulating the patient, this is correct. But the patient can have the feeling—the subjective feeling—of being free from pain for a long, long time. And when the pain does hit, it seems to hit and then disappear right away, even though it may last ten minutes of real time. It seems to last only a moment or two—ten seconds at the most—and then it disappears. The painful time is very short, and the time of being free from pain is very, very long; and so the patient's sense of time has been very greatly changed.

In this matter of inducing trances, the average user of hypnosis is rather wary, curious, concerned and sometimes even fearful about the length of time that is involved in inducing a trance. Well, how much time should be taken in inducing a trance? Just consider your own behavior and that of other normal people. How long does it take some people to go to sleep—something that has happened from the beginning of time. You put your head down on the pillow, and then the alarm clock rings and you have to look around and realize that a whole night has passed, and yet you are totally unaware of it. How many people take a tremendous pride in falling to sleep the moment their heads hit the pillow? They are willing to go to sleep when their heads hit the mattress if they don't need the pillow! It is a perfectly normal pride and very desirable pride. One wants the patient to take pride in his sense of time, his use of time.

Attitudes in Hypnosis

Confidence and Expectancy in Facilitating Trance Experience; No Need for Unsolicited Explanations or Qualifications: "Getting Down to Business!"

In hypnosis the most important thing in the development of a trance is not what you do but the attitude that you take toward your patient and that you allow the patient to take toward you. I think that every one of you ought to take an attitude that you know more than the patient does; you are much more experienced, you are trained in your particular specialty, you know what to do, or at least have a pretty good idea of what needs to be done or investigated to meet certain patients' problems.

You ought to have an attitude of confidence and expectancy, and you certainly ought to know that the patient is coming to you because he has a feeling of confidence in you. If, however, you take the attitude, "Well, *maybe* I can handle this sort of problem but I'm just not certain, and maybe somebody else could do it better," I think you had better refer that patient to somebody else, because certainly your frame of mind is utterly wrong. Whether it is pulling a tooth, or putting in sutures, or inducing a trance, you take the attitude: *I can really sew this laceration ... I can really fill this tooth ... I can really do a nice extraction.* You ought to take the same attitude toward asking your patient to develop a trance state.

Now, too many of us have the feeling that we have to go through a certain traditional ritual in developing a trance state. How many things do you need to say to a patient to ask him to develop a trance state? The patient comes into your office for hypnotic therapy. Do you really have to tell him that you are going to use hypnosis when that is the reason he has come to you? It is already understood. He knows why he has come, and you know why he has come, and you really do not need to enter into a general explanation of why he has come.

Nor do you need to go into a detailed explanation of your qualifications. The patient comes to me for psychiatric treatment. If he wants to ask me questions about my training, that is perfectly all right. He is entitled to do so, but if he is willing to take me at face value—well, that is perfectly all right, too. But I certainly am not going to waste his time by explaining that I went through the University of Wisconsin Medical School, and that I had such-and-such psychiatric training, and that I have taught psychiatry, and all that sort of thing. That is a sheer waste of time—his time and my time. He has come for psychiatric therapy, so let's get right down to business!

I said this morning that I was going to call on some unexpected subjects, and I intend to call on them for some very definite reasons.

All of you encounter the patient as he comes off the street. He comes in uncertain because he is troubled about his condition. He is worried about it, and he is legitimately worried because he doesn't know whether you or anybody else can really handle that kind of a problem. It is your obligation to teach him that you are delighted to see him, and that this is a problem that is going to interest you—that *does* interest you—because you feel rather confident that you can handle it. You don't expect to be absolutely perfect, but you do expect to do a good job, and you expect to meet his wishes, and you expect him to do his full share. That is the attitude you ought to take toward any patient who comes into your office.

DEMONSTRATION

Rossi: The demonstration that follows illustrates Erickson's highly original and characteristic use of open-ended questions to induce trance and to evoke and explore hypnotic phenomena in a permissive manner. It is fascinating to note how closely Erickson's questions and simple statements often echo the subject's remarks in a classical Rogerian manner. Erickson, however, always insisted that his "indirect" approach was fundamentally different from Roger's "non-directive" approach in that Erickson often had a firmly directive intent behind his apparent indirection.[11]

Questions Evoking Trance and Hypnotic Phenomena

Erickson: Now I am going to call on someone who does not expect to be called on. How do you do? How long do you think it will take you to go into a trance?

Subject: I'm not sure.

Erickson: You're really not sure, are you? What do you think will be the first thing you will demonstrate in a trance?

Subject: [*Shakes head.*]

Erickson: You're really not sure of that either, are you? Now, do you think you are really in the ordinary state of awareness?

Subject: Not completely.

Erickson: Not completely. How much of a trance do you think you are in? How fully aware do you think you are?

Subject: I'm aware of what?

Erickson: Now, I am drawing this out very deliberately, very carefully, so that the audience can notice certain things about you. [*Inaudible*] But have you any awareness of the fact that there is a lack of mobility on your part? Are you aware of the fact that your feet reflect the change? Are you aware of the fact that you can shake your head no, and that you continue shaking it just a little bit too long? And aren't you awfully still? Now why is your right hand cataleptic? And why isn't your left hand cataleptic? Did I do anything to make the right hand cataleptic?

Subject: No.

Erickson: Did I do anything to make your left hand non-cataleptic?

Subject: No.

Erickson: I lifted both of them, didn't I? Why did one go down and the other stay up? What mental

processes went on within you that enabled you to perceive that your right hand would be cataleptic and that your left hand would not be? You really don't know, do you? But you are aware that your right hand is cataleptic. Do you suppose your left hand will start lifting up toward your face?
Subject: Possibly.
Erickson: Possibly. How would you find that out? When did you find that out? You know, yet how will you find it out? Think about it. What else? What else? Now as you look at me and you listen to me, tell me, how easy has it been to forget that there is an audience present? Is the audience of any importance at all?
Subject: No.
Erickson: Isn't this the first time you have stood in front of an audience so wholly unconcerned about them? And would you like to watch your eyes close slowly? Now . . . and as they close, I want to call your attention to certain things.

Facilitating Trance

Recognizing Minimal Physiological Cues and Reinforcing Behavioral Possibilities; Utilizing Interest in Autogenic Training; Rapid Hypnotic Learning via Time Distortion, Anesthesia, Hypermnesia; Many Possibilities of Response

Erickson: Your pupils are dilating. There is an outer focus to your eyes, and slowly your lids are going down. You are not going to be aware of that at first. There will be a slow development within your own mind, and then perhaps there will be, first, the mental process of the eyes closing, and then there will be the physical process, and then finally there will be the physical process with the eyes remaining shut.

And now you know and I know that communication can be carried on through the simple process of nodding and shaking the head. It is very easy to communicate that way. And one of the things that is characteristic of developing a trance state is the matter of the time lag. There is an alteration of the understanding of time, and so one can nod the head slowly, and keep on slowly nodding the head, without being aware of the fact that one is doing so. The respiratory movements change markedly. Your swallowing reflex is gone; you can have it back any time you want to. It is really of no importance. You can have an anesthesia, if it is important to you. I do not know if you are musically inclined, but you might like to hear music in the distance or close by, or you might want to have a tune run through your head. Or you can get back to your sleep.

You might like to have a lost, lost memory come rushing into your mind with the greatest capacity for reflection. I would like to have you learn everything you can. One of the reasons I picked you out was this: I had advance knowledge that you are interested in autogenic training. I am delighted to hear that. I hope you have read Schultz and Luthe's book with a great deal of understanding. I'd like to have you realize that that book is expressive of the slow, painstaking, methodical, all-comprehensive orientation of the German scientist.

Schultz first developed autogenic training. He used the method of [*inaudible*] in using hypnosis, and he tried to adapt and derive understanding of what sort of psychological processes were involved [in hypnotic work] and developed autogenic training. I think the average person with autogenic training can learn in a much more rapid fashion. I think with this hypnotic knowledge, you learn all of the phases and stages of autogenesis a great deal more rapidly and comfortably.

That is what I would like to have you do. I would like to have you spend that length of time that is satisfactory to you. I would like to have you realize that you can learn some parts of it rapidly and that other parts you learn slowly—either rapidly or slowly according to clock time, or rapidly or slowly according to subjective time.

Trance Awakening

Hand Levitation Ratifying Trance

Erickson: Now, I would like you to have the experience of arousing from hypnotic trance. Do you think you are out of trance?
Subject: Not completely.
Erickson: What makes you think you are not completely?
Subject: My hand is still up.
Erickson: Your hand is still up. That is an interesting feeling, isn't it? I notice that your hand is beginning to awaken some. Did you notice that?
Subject: I don't know if I noticed it [myself], or if I noticed it after you said it.
Erickson: You don't know when you noticed it. And tell me, how long do you think it will take to wake up, wide awake!
Subject: Several more minutes.
Erickson: How long have you studied autogenic training?
Subject: About a year.

Questions Reinducing Trance Indirectly

Associating Trance with Turning Thoughts Inward; Force Fields and Polarities Ratifying Trance

Erickson: About a year. And what particular feature are you studying now? [*Pause*] Close your eyes.

[*To audience*] How does one induce a trance and reinduce a trance? I was awakening him. I asked him a perfectly legitimate question about something that he was studying. What did it do? It made him turn his thoughts inward and he started to examine his own memories and understandings and feelings. Then I said, "Close your eyes." *Close your eyes* is associated with the trance state, and the trance state was immediately reintroduced. How does one deepen a trance? There is your willingness to do that sort of thing! Now, I think he is going to rouse up again.

Erickson: Do start now. Now, how do you feel about my re-introducing the trance state?
Subject: It surprised me.
Erickson: It surprised you. Did you realize you could go into a trance that quickly?
Subject: No, but I have been learning during the past couple of days.
Erickson: You have been learning over the past couple of days. Did you realize you could stand up in front of an audience and go into a trance that quickly? You believe it now. How quickly can go into a trance? Let's put the question negatively: Could you stay out of a trance if you closed your eyes?
Subject: [*Closes eyes.*]

[*To audience*] A simple question honestly asked and honestly answered: "Could you stay out of a trance if you closed your eyes?" Now, there is only one possible way to answer that question, and that means that he has to make a first step, which is to close his eyes. When he makes the first step, the second step is so much easier. But all of you saw his face changing before he closed his eyes, and all of you, I think, knew that he was going to go into a trance.

Erickson: And now for the rest of the afternoon, I would like to have you feel rested and refreshed, as if you had been through a thoroughly competent, satisfying autogenic experience—one that would please you immensely. Now, get comfortable, rouse up, wide awake.

Hi! I think it is interesting to give your body time to awaken even after your mind is awake. If you consider the force field of the body (or whatever it is called—it was identified at Yale University), the polarity that is in all living tissue and can be recorded, you find out that it takes about five minutes for the magnetic force of the body to return to the normal waking state. That ought to be an interesting experience for you—since you are studying autogenic training—to sense the return of the normal polarity, the electric currents in your body.

Rossi: Erickson's early experimental work on hypnosis led him to believe that any extensive internal review of memories—particularly when they are reviewed in serial order from beginning to end—is trance inducing. See the first two papers in Volume I of Erickson, 1980. For a detailed discussion of "force fields" and hypnosis, see Ravitz, 1950.

Literalism and Confusion in Hypnosis

Erickson: Thank you so much.
Subject: [*Does not get up to leave*]
Erickson: Now, everybody here in the audience knows that when I said, "Thank you so much," I was dismissing the subject. Why didn't he leave?

[*To audience*] I am using this example to illustrate the tremendous need for you to be aware that the patient understands you in an exceedingly literal fashion. Although all of you could understand by implication that I had dismissed the

49

subject, if you examine my every word on the tape recorder, you will find that I didn't really *literally* dismiss him. All of you thought I had dismissed him, but he was listening, and he was understanding what I said in the true sense of the word—not the implication of the word. That is why I want you to learn how to write out suggestions, how to examine them, and how to figure out exactly what they mean.

Some of you have read my article on the confusion technique.[12] I didn't work out that technique in five minutes or ten minutes. I worked out that technique over a long, long period of time—months and months of assiduous work—trying to figure out just exactly how to arrange sentences to bring about a state of confusion in a person.

Yes, I can bring about a state of confusion in a person. There was that poor, unfortunate soul who walked around the corner of that building on a very windy day, and I was bracing myself against the wind. He bumped into me, and I promptly hauled out my watch and said, "It is exactly ten minutes of two." It was really four o'clock, and a block away he was still looking at me, wondering if a head shrinker shouldn't come and see me!

Now that was a very nice way of bringing about a state of confusion. You do it quickly, but you do it to the advantage of the other person. In hypnosis you want to use the confusion technique to the advantage of the patient. Therefore, you word your confusion technique in such a way that *it allows the patient to rearrange and rearrange and rearrange his own thinking until he is ready to accept his own clear thinking.*

Rossi: This idea is reminiscent of Erickson's important statement about the essence of hypnotherapy quoted above. We repeat it here for emphasis:

"The induction and maintenance of a trance serves to provide a special psychological state in which patients can reassociate and reorganize their inner psychological complexities and utilize their own capacities in a manner in accord with their own experiential life. Hypnosis does not change people nor does it alter

their past experiential life. It serves to permit them to learn more about themselves and to express themselves more adequately.

"Direct suggestion [authoritarian] is based primarily, if unwittingly, upon the assumption that whatever develops in hypnosis derives from the suggestions given. It implies that the therapist has the miraculous power of effecting therapeutic changes in the patient, and disregards the fact that *therapy results from an inner resynthesis of the patient's behavior achieved by the patient himself*. It is true that direct suggestion can effect alteration in the patient's behavior and result in a symptomatic cure, at least temporarily. However, such a 'cure' is simply a response to the suggestion and does not entail that reassociation and reorganization of ideas, understandings, and memories so essential for an actual cure. It is this experience of reassociating and reorganizing his own experiential life that eventuates in a cure, not the manifestation of responsive behavior which can, at best, satisfy only the observer." [Italics added] (p. 38)

This wonderfully clear statement could be regarded as the essence of the basic difference between the older authoritarian approaches to hypnosis that are based on direct suggestion versus Erickson's clinically permissive, naturalistic approach that depends on the patient's own "reassociating and reorganizing of his own experiential life." Ironically, most current-day experimentalists who believe they are in the vanguard of "modern research" on hypnosis by using standardized scales of "hypnotic susceptibility" are actually, like the general public, still adhering firmly to the naive, authoritarian view of hypnosis as some sort of programmed response to direct or covert suggestion.

DEMONSTRATION

Utilizing Personal Motivations to Overcome Stage Fright

Erickson: Now I am going to call on another subject—a very delightful subject. Mary, you are somewhere in the audience. I can see you very plainly. Mary, what do you think of my calling you in this unexpected way?

Subject: Somewhat surprised.

Erickson: You are a very good singer, aren't you?

Subject: That is a matter of opinion.

Erickson: What is your personal opinion?

Subject: Yes.

Erickson: Now, that settles it, and why don't you enjoy it?

Subject: I am afraid of people.

Erickson: Even these?

Subject: I really don't know.

Erickson: You really don't know, but you are nervous.

Subject: There is something about facing an audience that is inhibiting.

Erickson: Something about an audience that is inhibiting. Do you see what you have just done? You have crossed your legs away from me and you have put your arms behind you.

Subject: I am resisting.

Erickson: You are resisting. Now, do you really need to hang onto that chair?

Subject: Feet on the floor.

Erickson: Feet on the floor. Hands on your lap. Do you need to hang one hand under the other?

Subject: No.

Erickson: Now, so many of the audience members think that they must tell their patients so meticulously, so politely, so courteously exactly what to do instead of talking to them in a casual, personal, conversational fashion. Now, certainly, I did not ask you to stop resisting me.

Subject: Once I knew what I was doing —

Erickson: I didn't even ask you to quit. Isn't that correct? Instead, *you* told me how to quit: hands on your lap; feet on the floor. You told me!

Subject: Even though I know—well, I was feeling a bit stupid. I felt I shouldn't do this [resist] after two days [of attending a hypnosis workshop].

Erickson: But aren't you entitled to that reaction when you are called on unexpectedly?

Subject: I hope so.

Erickson: I hope so, too. Now, one of the questions I would like to ask you is this: When you sing before an audience, you get rather tightened up—pretty badly tightened up.

Subject: When I am doing a completely disguised character, then I don't.

Erickson: When the character is completely disguised, then you don't. What do you mean by "disguised"?

Subject: I mean playing something other than straight—or standing up at a microphone, singing—if I am doing a musical of some sort and am dressed in another costume.

Erickson: So that you are not recognizable?

Subject: Recently, as a witch, I was completely disguised!

Erickson: You certainly would be!

Subject: That role came very easily, for there was no fear.

Erickson: Uh-huh.

Subject: I had a few breakthroughs here and there—really, there are situations you can't get away from—such as audiences.

Erickson: All right. What kind of an audience could you sing to?

Subject: I haven't figured that out yet.

Erickson: You haven't.

Subject: The only thing I have discovered so far is that when I am secluded [in a costume], I'm much better.

Erickson: You are the evil witch who can face [*inaudible*]. How would you like to speak to an audience of witches? Now wouldn't that be charming? It certainly would be. Which of those witches out there do you want to see?

Subject: That's not fair.

Erickson: I know it isn't, but someone has to take that honor.

Subject: Okay. Actually, none of them looks like a witch.

Erickson: You are not trying hard enough, because I can see the witches there. The best way is to close your eyes when you look at them. Does that choice surprise you?

Subject: No.

Erickson: All right, let's be more tangible. Have you always known that you appreciated that particular quality in a person? You are very, very comfortable now, and yet there must be some kind of agony in those muscles to hold them there comfortably. And there must be something you want to do in that very, very comfortable tightening of muscles in your arms that holds your arms comfortably. Perhaps you want to transfer that comfortable feeling to the diaphragmatic area. That is quite a job to learn, isn't it? But you can learn it bit by bit. The right hand goes down toward your lap and ends there. Isn't it an interesting feeling the way that tight feeling in your diaphragm [*pause*] is leaving? What is happening? Do you think it is working?

Subject: I would like to think —

Erickson: [*Inaudible*]

Subject: I feel great.

Erickson: You're feeling great. You know, I am tone deaf and I used to date a girl who loved to sing. And she always enjoyed dating me because she always sang off-key. I couldn't tell the difference. I enjoyed seeing her so happy. I didn't mind her being off-key, on-key, under-key, beside-the-key, or whatever key it was!

Are you comfortable? Do you know the male term for *witch*? Some people think the Wizard of Oz is a good term for a male witch. But there is a special name, and I can't remember what it is.

Subject: Warlock.

Erickson: That's right! The masculine form of *witch* is *warlock*. That's right. The next time you sing, would you like to sing to a bunch of warlocks?

Subject: I think it would be great.

Erickson: I think it would be great, too. And you can really run the range of all the tones of which you are capable. Tell me, do you think it is possible to look at you and not be —

Subject: It's possible.

Erickson: But not likely. Do you think it is possible for you to get a compliment like that in front of an audience and react so slightly as that? Usually, you would be embarrassed. What happened to you? Do you often feel like that before a warlock?

Subject: No . . . no . . . no.

Erickson: You can see there are warlocks in this room, and if they happen to bring their spouses, the witches, who cares? When are you going to have the pleasure of finding this out?

Subject: The ninth of June.

Erickson: Are you right- or left-handed?

Subject: Almost ambidextrous, but I write with my right hand.

Erickson: Can you write with your left hand?

Subject: I was pretty much held back.

Erickson: You feel pretty much held back. Would you mind writing me a left-handed letter?

Subject: No, I would be glad to write you a left-handed letter.

Erickson: Would you comment in the letter about how much you enjoyed singing to that bunch of warlocks and witches?

Subject: I guarantee that by the ninth of June, you will have a letter.

Erickson: How will you address it?

Subject: To Dr. Erickson, Phoenix. Everyone knows that!

Erickson: What was he called in *Faust?*

Subject: Methuselah?

Erickson: No. Somebody else. Do you like Faust?

Subject: I like all sorts of music.

Erickson: Now suppose you write a left-handed letter to Methuselah Erickson, telling me how much you enjoyed singing to a group of warlocks and witches!

Subject: Agreed.

Erickson: Put your hand where you are going to feel an awful lot of comfort as you sing. It is a nice feeling, isn't it?

Subject: Yes.

[*To audience*] You know, I think it is an awfully important thing for anybody who uses hypnosis to have a number of techniques that are unrecognizable to the patient. I invariably touch a patient in some way, because sometimes the patient may have had a traumatic experience that frightens them out of contact with me. Therefore, I have no hesitation about taking hold of the patient's hand and asking: "May I lift your arm up and put it on the arm of the chair?" But by the time I get the arm up there, catalepsy is present, so I have to establish one sort of contact. Then I can very carefully, slowly move a pencil in some silly, meaningless fashion. Patients strive and struggle to put a meaning to that meaningless movement. Then later when I do the same thing, I reawaken that visual contact and they strive to put a meaning to it like before, and they reach out for any meaning I offer to them.

Then, if I happen to be holding a microphone, I just automatically shift the microphone in various ways that holds their attention and causes them to shift back and forth. Mary did very, very nicely in noticing that I had done it to the other gentleman as I did with her.

Now, in the psychological laboratory, you learn that by combining 15 or 16 stimuli, you can build up a conditioned response. Yet you can take the primitive, naive savage who has never seen an electric stove, and you show him that red griddle on the electric stove, and he touches it just once and gets a conditioned response for the rest of his life! How many conditioned stimuli do you need? In the laboratory situation, you can get one sort of behavior; in the life situation, another sort of behavior.

In medical school you learn that *in vitro* [in the test tube] is one sort of thing and *in vivo* [in the living organism] is another sort of thing. Therefore, when you are dealing with a living human being—somebody who can sit there and feel and understand—you do not treat that person as you would a culture medium that requires so many days for the culture to form. You don't treat that patient as you would the unmotivated psychologist who is learning to develop a conditioned response. Your patient has a different kind of motivation than the volunteer subject in the psychology laboratory or the physiology laboratory. You recognize that the motivation of your patient is a tremendously important thing, and you ought to have no hesitation in bringing it about.

Relaxation Training and Posthypnotic Suggestion

Questions Evoking New Sensations, Catalepsy, Anesthesia, and Stopped Seeing?

Erickson: Mary, if you stop to think it over, I have taken you cold before a strange audience. I'd like to have you mention so many things.
Subject: Yesterday I probably would have —
Erickson: And when I mentioned your midriff in front of this group, when I asked where you felt

[tension], where did you put your hand?
Subject: On my midriff.
Erickson: Could you have done that yesterday?
Subject: No.
Erickson: What is the difference between yester-day and today?
Subject: I am feeling so much more relaxed.
Erickson: You are feeling so much more relaxed. And, really, you can't tell whether that relaxation is in your feet, your ankles, your head, your thighs, your fingers, your wrists, your forearms, your up-per arms, your shoulders, your chest, your abdo-men, or where it is. Why do you suppose you picked out your face as the first place of recogni-tion?
Subject: I just felt warm.
Erickson: As if you're feeling embarrassed again, but this time feeling warm without the embarrass-ment.
Subject: It is a strange feeling—I have never had it before.
Erickson: When you stop to think of it, the audi-ence doesn't look half bad.
Subject: No.
Erickson: What do you suppose you will do before you go to bed tonight?
Subject: Relax.
Erickson: What else?
Subject: Just before, or when?
Erickson: Sometime before you go to bed and after you eat dinner tonight.
Subject: I don't know.
Erickson: That is right, you don't really know. Would you like to have me tell you?
Subject: Yes.
Erickson: Remember, Methuselah can tell you a lot of things. I think you are going to be surprised by having something come to your mind, or finding among sheets of music some piece of music you

haven't thought of for a long, long time that was really very, very pleasurable to you. Some series of notes, some sheet of music, some melody. I don't really know how to describe it, but something of musical significance and value, peculiar to you as a personality, will come flooding into your mind with the greatest of ease and pleasure and satisfaction. So utterly pleasing, so delightful, so relaxing. *Somewhere in that piece of music is going to be an utterly charming note. And that is the last thing you will hear—a slow fading out of that note as you drift off into a nice, comfortable sleep.* Yes, when you are about to fall asleep that note will recur, and then slowly fade out as you go into physiological sleep. Does that sound all right? Tell me, *do you think that you have an anesthesia?*

Subject: *I don't know.*

Erickson: You can't tell. Can you stand up?

Subject: No.

Erickson: You have a saddle block. How does it feel to develop a saddle block that easily and that quickly? You can answer me now.

Subject: No effort.

Erickson: No effort at all to develop a saddle block. *Does it surprise you to know the capacity you have in altering your sensory behavior?*

Subject: Yes.

Erickson: Now I am going to do the opposite to you of what you have been doing to yourself. In the past you have tied up your midriff, your diaphragm, and now it is loose, relaxed, and comfortable, is it not? Can you move your hips now? No? Yet in the back of your mind you know that the movement in your hips is only temporarily stopped, just as you can temporarily stop the movement of your diaphragm. You could have corrected me then—right now—by slowly changing your mind. You can start moving your wrist, and how does that feel? But that wasn't your thought, was it? You realize

you have a lot of control, haven't you? *And would you like to remove your saddle block now and get the freedom of movement back in your body?*
Subject: Yes.
Erickson: All right. *Your wishes are my command.*
Subject: I can see all of the audience now.
Erickson: Isn't it delightful to see them? Take a good look at that audience, and enjoy every bit of it—all untroubled, unafraid, and delighted with it.
Subject: It is different, tremendously different.

Rossi: In this section we witness a very typical example of how Erickson uses open-ended questions to facilitate the exploration of new sensations and perceptions so that the subject is able to say, "It is a strange feeling—I have never had it before."

Erickson then utilizes her interest in music to hear "an utterly charming note" within herself as a post-hypnotic signal to "drift off into a nice, comfortable sleep." It is all done in such an indirect and casual manner that one hardly knows that a posthypnotic suggestion has been given.

Sleep is naturally associated with complete unawareness of sensation, so within this context Erickson asks a fail-safe question that may or may not evoke an anesthesia: " . . . Do you think that you have an anesthesia?" Her response of "I don't know" is highly characteristic of the hypnotic subject who is open to further orientation.

Erickson provides this orientation with one of his favorite questions, "Can you stand up?" Since she responds with, "No," he can assume she is experiencing a catalepsy which he labels as a "saddle block." This was a common term in use at the time and understood by most women to denote a kind of chemically induced anesthesia for childbirth.

Erickson utilizes this apparently dramatic alteration in her sensations and perceptions to reinforce her ability to learn to relax her diaphragm and "get the freedom of movement back in [her] body."

Erickson then arranges it so that he can easily say, "Your wishes are my command." Is this an inside joke? Perhaps, but it is also a reflection of his therapeutic attitude: The hypnotherapist may facilitate the experience of all sorts of exotic hypnotic phenomena, but whatever the experience, it always works best within a positive therapeutic context wherein the subject/client is commanding by getting what he or she really wants and/or needs.

When the subject then says, "I can see all of the audience now," she is implying that she was not seeing them previously. This may be an example of what Erickson termed "stopped seeing." In a large audience hall, he reported that the visual field in some somnambulistic subjects (those capable of experiencing profound hypnotic phenomena while apparently awake) seemed to be limited to various arbitrary degrees. Some might see no further than the therapist; some, no further than the stage, and so forth.[14]

Protecting the Patient in Hypnosis

Reward and Minimal Cues; Utilizing Natural Processes of Behavior to Facilitate Catalepsy and Saddle Block Anesthesia; Avoiding Hypnotic Challenges

One of the things I teach my patients is that every time they accomplish a difficult task, they ought to reward themselves in some way. I can recall teaching my tiny little daughter, when she was only that high, to pat her knee and tell her knee what a good knee it was to stop hurting after the tumble she had taken. And she patted her knee and it stopped hurting. It was a good knee.

A year ago she broke her elbow, and the general practitioner said to this 12-year-old girl, in a very gentle and very thoughtful way: "You have a crack right through the elbow joint, but it is going to heal."

She looked at him so disgustedly and said: "Of course it will. It is a good elbow!"

She likes her elbow, and whenever she does anything of merit, she rewards herself in some particular way. Sometimes it is by reading a special story that she has put away. Sometimes it is by writing a letter to Grandma or Grandpa. Sometimes it is by working out a practical joke to play on her father or her mother or her friend the dog. But it is always something pleasing.

> *Erickson:* You have a task to do before you go to bed tonight. Before you go sound asleep, you have to reward yourself.
> *Subject:* I shall sing a song.
> *Erickson:* And who will hear it first?
> *Subject:* Probably my coach.
> *Erickson:* It will probably lift him right off his chair. Thank you very much.

Question: Would you give us a rationale of what you did with this subject?
Erickson: It would be easier if I could hear the tape recording of it. I play things by ear.

One of the things I did was to demonstrate immediately that I wasn't the least bit afraid of the total situation. I was willing to call anything by name. I was willing to laugh and to joke. I put forth a challenge on what the masculine form of witches was; I had the mistaken idea that it was *wizard* rather than *warlord*. I started her thinking in her own mind, and then each little thing that I did was in some way intended to emphasize, confirm, reaffirm.

Why did I bring about that saddle block [anesthesia]? Do you suppose that saddle block was a very convincing experience to her? She really found out that she couldn't move. But, you see, she knows what a saddle block is; so let's have her have a very, very convincing experience without her knowing how on earth I suggested it to her. Now she has that experience *within herself.* It is part of her own experience. It belongs to her, and there is no way that she or you can say that I suggested to her.

What did I really do? How responsive are we to minimal cues? To minimal feelings? She told me all about her response to the microphone movements, so I suddenly rigidified the microphone movement; and that in turn rigidified her eyeball movement, rigidified her head movement, rigidified her neck movement, rigidified her shoulder movement. Everything got rigidified, on its own, all the way down to a saddle block!

You start with the eyeballs. She has already told me about the eyeballs. I heard her; I understood; and I simply followed it out, and *she followed her own natural processes of behavior.* Therefore, it wasn't necessary for me to go through a long, laborious process of explaining to her what a saddle block was and how to develop it and what she would experience. All I needed to do was to utilize that one little thing she told me she had observed that gentleman from the audience do. She had seen him do it. She is fully as competent, mentally, as he is. If he can do it, she can do it, and so can you. Why shouldn't I bear that in mind and remember it? Then very, very quietly, even though all of you watched me, you never saw the rigidity with which I held my coat and how I could move my head or anything, but that microphone was still steady.

Question: Could you make Mary sing a song right here if you wanted to, in spite of the fact that you said she was frightened before an audience?

Erickson: I worked with Mary for Mary's benefit, not for the benefit of the audience. I want Mary to mull it all over in her own unconscious mind, and to think it over, and to incorporate it into her thinking. Then I can be sure that Mary is going to [sing in front of an audience]. *I am not going to put her in a challenging situation.*

Question: But it would be good for her to do that, wouldn't it?

Erickson: No, it would not be good for her. I have already set up the situation for her in terms of what she is going to do tonight. She is really going to enjoy a note of music. That is her right, that is her privilege; and her rights and her privileges are greater than those of the audience.

In the privacy of your office you work for the patient's

benefit. That is why you exclude the third person, because the third person does not really belong there. I asked Mary, *for her own benefit,* to have come to mind a piece of music (a melody, or some series of notes). I told her how ignorant I was on the subject of music so that Mary could think favorably of her knowledge of music, and I could tell her a perfectly truthful story about my ignorance of music—and yet it was a *personal* story. It was one story told by one person to another person. It was not a story told by an august personage to an inferior; it was just one person talking to another.

I asked Mary to demonstrate to the audience where she felt comfortable. I thought that was as far as I should really go, so far as the audience was concerned, because Mary had always related her tight midriff to an audience. Let her have the experience of relating a mood of comfortable midriff to an audience. But that is still an inner experience belonging to Mary, and the audience has to take Mary's word for it. It is *Mary* who needs to have a very comfortable feeling about her singing.

Question: You made her comfortable. You said she had never been so relaxed in front of an audience. Isn't the next step for her to sing then—under your guidance?

Erickson: Not necessarily. After helping her to become comfortable, what did I do? I tightened her up. If she is ever going to be tightened up, let me do the tightening. So I tightened her up and then I let *her* unloosen herself—which is the same thing [as having her sing in front of you], but *it does not constitute a challenge to her.*

> *Erickson:* Mary, do you think I handled that situation correctly?
> *Subject:* Yes. This way I trust you.

Erickson: Her answer brings up a beautiful point I always like to emphasize. *You are always exceedingly careful to protect your patient in every possible way.* You do have to attack your patient in certain ways. But you do it frankly, and you do it in a way that let's her know that you are genuinely interested, and then you start protecting her so that she realizes

64

that your attack on her was not a vicious attack. It is like the surgeon who must do certain things in order to suture a wound. The dentist may have to use a scalpel to loosen a tooth before he extracts it, but the patient knows that the dentist is inflicting that hurt for the purpose of reducing a bigger hurt, and therefore the patient accepts the dentist.

Rossi: Here again we witness the apparent paradox whereby Erickson facilitates freedom and creative choice within a context of manipulation. Notice the vociferousness of the questioner's attitude in challenging Erickson to "prove for the audience" that he had helped the subject by having her sing for the audience. For Erickson this kind of request/demand was anathema; he was concerned with protecting the patient by allowing her to practice alone at home *for her benefit* rather then singing for the benefit of the audience.

This challenge by the questioner is indicative of why hypnosis acquired a negative connotation of manipulation. All too often, stage hypnotists (and even some professional therapists) have used hypnosis to prove something for others rather then for the patient. Perhaps a great deal of the so-called unreliability of hypnosis is due to patients rebelling in conscious and unconscious levels against such exploitative presumption.

DEMONSTRATION

Minimal Cues of Trance Induction

Question: Why did you suggest the left-handed letter rather than a right-handed one?

Erickson: That is one of the nicest questions that has been asked. Would you come up please?

While I was looking at you, do you know what I was thinking? I was thinking, *There is a woman I would like to have as a subject.*

Subject: Why?

Erickson: How good a subject to you think you are?

Subject: I don't think I am too good a subject because I am too scared.

Erickson: You're too scared. How scared are you?

Subject: Well, I couldn't produce self-hypnosis yesterday. And when you have failed once, you think you are incapable.

Erickson: Would you like to follow Mary? What did she do to go into a trance?

Subject: Closed her eyes.

Erickson: I asked her to close her eyes and she went into a trance. Is that really correct?

Subject: I don't remember too much.

Erickson: Do you suppose that was why you were able to ask that awfully important question [about the left-handed letter]?

Subject: I don't know how important it was. I was just curious.

Erickson: How did you know if being left-handed or right-handed pertained to Mary's trance?

Subject: I didn't know that—that was why I asked.

Erickson: Have you ever been right- or left-handed?

Subject: I am right-handed, but I can write with my left hand.

Erickson: You can write with your left hand.

Subject: Not too well.

Erickson: Not too well, but you told me that when you asked the question.

Subject: I did?

Erickson: That is why it was the most delightful question you ever asked me—because you told me so much. Right-handed people are strictly right-handed and would not have asked that question. They would have no way of asking that question.

I took hold of Mary's hand like this, remember? And it stayed right there, and then I asked her to close her eyes. That's right. And, now, to let me know that you are beginning to understand what it feels like to go into a trance, your left hand is slowly rising up and touching your face . . . .Now a littler jerk . . . and then another jerk . . . and then another . . . and the elbow bends now. And when the left hand goes up, the right hand goes down an equal amount. You don't really like hanging on to those doubts, do you?

Subject: No, I don't.

Erickson: Slowly your right hand moves over to where your left hand should be by now . . . slowly past the midline of your body to where you think your left hand should be. And it is really very hard to keep the movement of your hand secret from yourself, isn't it?

Subject: Is it moving?

Erickson: Yes, it's moving. And it is all right for you to know that it is moving. You don't have to keep it a secret. Your elbows moved a little closer to your body. In the privacy of my office, this is done much more rapidly and more easily. But you are aware of that, are you not?

Subject: Yes.

Erickson: Did I give you any help?

Subject: I don't know.

Erickson: You don't know. What is happening?

Subject: I don't think anything is happening.

Erickson: Why do you keep your hands up there?

Subject: Because you told me to put them up there.

Erickson: Are you in the habit of having strange men lift your arms up?

Subject: I thought I was supposed to do that.

Erickson: Can you keep your eyes open?

Subject: I suppose they will close eventually.

[*To audience*] Did you watch her face and notice that there has been an ironing out of her facial expression? Did you notice that her expression tends to limit itself to the eyes entirely; that she is keeping a very rapid movement of her eyes; that her mouth has lost a lot of its mobility; that her cheeks have lost a lot of their mobility? She has lost the mobility of her hands; there has been a change in her respiratory rhythm; there has been a change in her swallowing reflex; there has been a change in the mobility of her head. And even though I am talking about her to the audience, there hasn't been the self-conscious responses that she made previously. And I am still talking about her, and she hears everything I say, but in some peculiar way, the self-consciousness has disappeared. It is true. She is free of her self-consciousness from the audience.

Coping with Resistance to Trance

Utilizing Questions with the Negative to
Facilitate a Positive Response

Erickson: You never thought about it [handedness]. You never thought about it, and yet you spoke about it here.
Subject: Yes, that's true.
Erickson: I know what you mean now, and now that feeling is coming back, isn't it?
Subject: Yes.
Erickson: How did it come back to you?
Subject: I don't know.
Erickson: You don't know how it came back.
Subject: I didn't need it anymore.
Erickson: You didn't need it anymore. I touched your forehead. I was very careful about that. Now, do you notice that that feeling is comfortable?
Subject: Yes.
Erickson: The question that you asked is so important. I got the accidental information from Mary

that once she was left-handed. For a long time, Mary has wanted to sing in public. Long ago she was deprived of something—*left-handed writing*—so I simply tied the two together. It was so easily done, for she could write that letter with her left hand, and it is tied to singing. She couldn't see me tie it to the singing, and neither could anybody else. But I tied the two together, and I am not the least bit afraid of telling Mary. Your unconscious didn't understand that [association], and yet your unconscious understood it well enough to ask me that highly important question.

How did I do it? You recognized in some way, consciously, that that left-handed writing had something to do with Mary's singing. Now, when do you really want to go into a trance?

Subject: I don't know that I really do.

Erickson: Do you want to bet that sometime in your life you won't want to go into a trance?

Subject: No.

Erickson: I don't want to bet either. Sometime in your life you may want desperately to go into a deep trance, and how long is it going to take you?

Subject: I don't know that either.

Erickson: Any longer than it took Mary?

Subject: I am not too inclined to go into a trance today.

Erickson: Yes, that's right. I said that "sometime" you may be desperately eager to go into a trance. How long does it take you? Just about as quickly as you answered that question about the left-handed writing. It is just that easy. How do you feel about the audience?

Subject: Not as much as when I first came up.

Erickson: How do they look?

Subject: The way the light is shining, they look far away—except the men here.

Erickson: Except the men here. Are you disturbed in any way?

Subject: No, just a little self-conscious.
Erickson: Is it all right if I let you feel self-conscious?
Subject: It's not comfortable.
Erickson: It's not? Don't you think they [the audience members] had better learn how to deal with a self-conscious patient?
Subject: Yes, definitely.
Erickson: I haven't really tried to ease your self-consciousness.
Subject: No, not completely.
Erickson: Are you angry?
Subject: No.
Erickson: Do you mind not relieving your self-consciousness?
Subject: No. I think you have a point there.
Erickson: Sometimes when we are self-conscious, we are in pain or distress. How is your self-conscious distress?
Subject: Not quite as bad as it was a moment ago.
Erickson: Because we talked about it, isn't that right? We talked about it without any concern, without any fear, without any anxiety. And I'm perfectly certain your self-consciousness will disappear. *Are you going to try to prove me wrong?*
Subject: No.
Erickson: Now, tell me, and be very honest. Would you like to go into a trance now?
Subject: I don't know.
Erickson: You are in one right now, and that is an honest statement. It is quite different from your first statement ["I don't know that I really do"], isn't it?
Subject: Yes.
Erickson: How did I manage to switch you over from "I don't want to" to "I don't know"?
Subject: You put it into a learning situation.
Erickson: I put you in a learning situation. How else does one overcome resistance?
Subject: If you want to get rid of something, then you might go into a trance to accomplish that.

Erickson: While we were talking here, how many times have you forgotten the presence of the audience?

Subject: Not too often.

Erickson: How many times, though?

Subject: I don't know . . . I suppose so. I don't really know that I have.

Erickson: In other words, you have lost your self-consciousness so much that you were just paying attention to me. Isn't that right? How does it feel to come back in contact with the audience?

Subject: Fine.

Erickson: You are not concerned about your actions. You are more concerned about them. How does it feel when I take hold of your wrists? In what way do I jar them up? You suggest it by a slight movement, by a light touch, by not actually lifting them. That is an awfully important thing for the audience members to bear in mind. You touch, you suggest the direction of the movement. You leave the movement to the patient. You suggest the anesthesia to the patient, but you leave the anesthesia to the patient—just as Mary produced her own anesthesia.

What does a local spinal do to patients? It lessens their activity. They lose their sensation; they don't know how to move their legs. They become paralyzed, though they are not truly paralyzed. They have no feeling. They don't know how to move a part of the body they can't feel. And, really, how long do you think you'd like to be in a trance?

Subject: Ten minutes.

Erickson: How do you feel right now?

Subject: Not uncomfortable.

Erickson: Not uncomfortable.

Rossi: To cope with resistance to trance, Erickson simply continues with his questioning approach designed to explore areas of agreement and facilitate the possibility of inner experience even while the subject's conscious mind appears to be warding it off. In particular, notice Erickson's penchant for phrasing questions with a negative that evokes a positive implied agreement with him, even though the subject is expressing a "no" response to his question:

Erickson: Do you want to bet that sometime in your life you *won't* want to go into trance?
Subject: No. [Her answer implies that sometime she will!]
Erickson: Are you going to try to prove me wrong?
Subject: No. [Her answers implies that she will agree to Erickson being correct.]

Erickson frequently expressed the view that this was a way of letting the resistive patient "have her cake and eat it, too." Such patients can give vent to their need to resist while at the same time enjoying the benefits of therapy.[15]

DEMONSTRATION

Resolving Claustrophobia

Altering Perceptions, Thoughts, and Feelings

Erickson: Thank you very much for coming up here. How much am I at liberty to tell?
Subject: All you know.
Erickson: He's safe! How large a room is this?
Subject: I'd say, 50 feet by 125 feet.
Erickson: [*To audience*] Do any of you who do not know this gentleman know why I asked that question?
Audience Member: Does it have to do with dissociation?

Erickson: No.

Audience Member: Is he an architect?

Erickson: No.

Audience Member: Phobia?

Erickson: Right—claustrophobia. So what have I defined? That this is a nice, big room—a large room—one that he had to look way back there, and way over there, to way over there [to estimate the dimensions].

[*To subject*] I put you in a great big room. But if you were in my office, I would tell you that my office is really wider than nine-by-nine, and you would have to admit that it was about 12-by-12, and *I would let you enlarge it.* Then I would point out that alcove where I keep my nude dancing girls, and I would point out that arched door there, and I would add the closet to the room. Now, how large is the closet?

Subject: I wouldn't know unless I had opened it.

Erickson: That's right. It could be any size, so the room could be markedly larger. Then I could point out the door that leads to the boys' bedroom, because my office is in my home. How large is the boys' bedroom?

Subject: I wouldn't know that either.

[*To audience*] My 12-by-12 office would get larger and larger and larger. That is exactly the technique I employed with an exceedingly well-known, world renowned scientist who came to me for psychotherapy. He looked through the door of my office and said, "Your office is *this* small."

"Yes," I said. "With that closet door there shut, it is this small; with the drape over the window there, it is this small; with the door of the boys' bedroom there, it is this small; with the back door closed and the drape over it, it is this small.

"I guess I can come in," he answered.

I had admitted that my office was *this small,* but I had added all of the other enlargements. But I didn't say they were enlargements; *it was his interpretation that they were en-*

largements, and so he felt very comfortable.

Then I told him after he sat down: "Of course, you can still be uncomfortable in this office even though it is as large as it is, but we can make it as large as all outdoors. So let's move back the drapes on the window."

That office really became very, very large—it included all of outdoors. The window was still shut and it was midwinter, but why shouldn't I enlarge the room without telling the patient I was enlarging it?

When you are dealing with claustrophobic patients, you had better recognize their feelings, and you had better respect those feelings, but *you also had better let them start altering those feelings.*

Humor Discharging the
Symptomatology of Resistance

Erickson: You saw Mary come up here?
Subject: Yes, I did.
Erickson: Do you remember one of the questions I asked her?
Subject: I think you asked her if she was comfortable.
Erickson: What was one of the things I called to her attention?
Subject: The warmth of her face?
Erickson: No. I called her attention to the fact that she had her legs crossed away from me and that she had her hands in back of her. You are pretty well wrapped up in your own arms. See, you are gripping your hands.

[*To audience*] Instead of treating that resistance seriously, as if it were a desperately serious problem that had to be dealt with, why shouldn't I laugh about it? Why shouldn't the patient laugh about it? No reason at all, because patients really ought to show some resistance to you. They come to you, and they know that you are going to change them in some way, but they don't know how. They have no idea of how thoroughly you understand their problems; but they know very well that *they* don't understand their problems, so how could a perfect stranger understand them? They are justified in having resistance. Therefore, *they ought to show that resistance as a part of their symptomatology, and the therapist ought to respect it, but he also ought to put it in its rightful place in a therapeutic situation.*

Symptom Shifts with State of Mind

Erickson: How large or how small a room could you be comfortable in?
Subject: It depends on my state of mind.
Erickson: It depends on the state of your mind. How high should the ceiling be?
Subject: There again, it depends. I prefer a rather high ceiling, and the number of exits depends on how obstructed I am from reaching them.
Erickson: You wouldn't want to sit in the far corner of a restaurant, would you?
Subject: Sometimes I wouldn't.
Erickson: Sometimes you would and sometimes you wouldn't. Why?
Subject: It depends on my state of mind. Sometimes I don't feel a problem when everything is going smoothly. When I have a lot on my mind, and I find myself in a situation in which my nerves aren't right, then even a large room can overpower me.
Erickson: Some of the time your state of mind is okay and a large room or a small room is all right. Sometimes a small room or a large room isn't all right.
Subject: That is right.

[*To audience*] What information has the subject given me? He has already told me very nicely, in his own words, that his problem is not a fixed and rigid and insoluble problem; that there are times when his nerves are alright, and times when his nerves are not alright.

Two-Level Communication

> *Erickson:* What are the things you do when your nerves are alright?
> *Subject:* I relax.
> *Erickson:* How do you relax?
> *Subject:* I can't really explain it [*subject crosses legs*].
> *Erickson:* You can't really explain it. Thanks for showing me —you crossed your legs and touched yourself.
> *Subject:* I can't relax with my feet on the floor and my hands separate.
> *Erickson:* That's right.
> *Subject:* I am much more relaxed with my legs crossed and my hands together.
> *Erickson:* Yes. Let's protect the situation.
> *Subject:* It's like sleeping on your back—it depends upon your frame of mind.

[*To audience*] I said, "Thanks for showing me." I asked him first, "How do you relax?" Well, how was he sitting? I asked him, "How do you relax?", and then I thanked him for showing me. That is communication at two different levels—communication at the conscious level and communication at the unconscious level.

Thinking and Doing in Phobia

Objective and Subjective Thinking; Elevator Kisses

> *Erickson:* How much hypnosis do you think you'll need to achieve a freedom from the disgusting qualities of fear and of claustrophobia?
> *Subject:* I think you'll have quite a problem. I think

it will be very hard to cure me of it—not that I won't lend myself as much as possible, because I will. But it's just so bad, and I am not familiar enough with your line of work.

Erickson: All right. Let's repeat what you said. You think I will have quite a problem—I think you're right. How much of a problem do you think you'll have?

Subject: Well, I have been fighting it for years.

Erickson: You have been fighting it for years. Wouldn't it be much better to get over fighting it?

Subject: Yes, absolutely.

Erickson: I think so, too, because the longer you fight things, the longer they last. The sooner you start getting well, the less fighting you will have to do. Well, how do you want to use that energy?

Subject: Show me how to cure it and I would be glad to use it.

Erickson: To cure it?

Subject: Yes.

Erickson: Let's be reasonable. Let's *lessen* it first. I think that would be a much better way of starting: to lessen it bit by bit—not to cure it, but to lessen it by degree, and by degrees you might not notice at first. Now, I don't know whether you are married or whether you have children.

Subject: I am married and I have children.

Erickson: You know, every time I go away from home for a week or more, when I come back my 13-year-old and 14-year-old daughters have grown, very definitely, a little bit taller. If I had stayed home that week, I wouldn't have noticed. I remember once I went away for a week and when I came back, my son, Allen, was a half inch taller than his mother. Then I made a second trip that lasted a week and a half, and when I came home he was taller than I was! I wouldn't have noticed that change [if I had been at home that week].

My youngest son came in one day and said, "Hello, Shortie." That was the first time I noticed that he was looking down at me, but he had been looking down at me for some time. He had noticed it because it was important to him.

But in the matter of your phobia, there isn't very much about it that you understand except the feeling that it gives you. You are awfully limited in your knowledge and understanding of the phobia.

Subject: I think I understand it.

Erickson: [*Inaudible*] You managed to grow quite a bit without understanding that it was due to the calcium in your milk. You didn't have to understand that there was calcium or protein or fat, but you grew just the same. In this matter of growing away from your phobia, do you really need to understand some of those things which belong to your past—to the remote past, and the forgotten past, and the unreachable past? Or would you like to have a sense of freedom today, tomorrow, next week, next month, next year, five years from now?

Subject: A sense of freedom when I get in elevators.

Erickson: How would that be to get rid of it five years from now?

Subject: I would welcome it.

Erickson: And, you know, one of the delights would be to ride in that elevator and have the electricity go off, and there is a pretty elevator girl right there! Have you ever thought about that?

Subject: I've tried all kinds of things.

Erickson: No, I mean to have this thing really happen—not just think about it.

Subject: I don't know. I'm afraid of what might happen—but not to the elevator girl!

Erickson: Well, wouldn't that be the *better* thing to think about?

Subject: I am sure you are right.

Erickson: You know, that is what I did to a doctor once. He was absolutely scared to get into an elevator, so I made my arrangement with the elevator girl, and I managed to see to it that the doctor was standing right there. I gave him a shove and got in the elevator with him. Halfway between floors the elevator stopped, the lights went out, and the elevator girl said, "Not you with the cane but the other guy. Where are you?"

He started to yell, but it wasn't because he was caught in an elevator! She said, "You can give me one awfully nice kiss, and I'll turn on the power and we will go on up to the tenth floor. This is the third floor. If you want to get off here, it will cost you several more kisses."

"But I'm a married man," my friend protested.

"I don't care," she replied. "Then you ought to know how to kiss better!"

That was the end of Hank's elevator phobia. It was a long time before he forgave me!

Why did I do that with Hank? For a very good reason. I knew Hank, and I knew a lot of his inhibitions, fears, and anxieties. I knew that he could live through the experience of the stopped elevator; I knew that he could live through that elevator girl's kiss. I knew that he could live through a half dozen of them. Once he had lived through it, Hank would very carefully take the elevator on the other side of the hall run by an old man. But he would take the elevator up to the 20th floor. That's right. That was his choice, and he wasn't going to ride with that girl again!

Subject: I think you'd have to know your patient pretty well.

Erickson: That is right. How well do you know yourself?

Subject: I know myself well enough not to try it that way!

Erickson: I don't think you should try it. You don't know yourself well enough. Have you ever walked up to the second floor and stood in front of the elevator door when the elevator wasn't in operation, and really used your intelligence to think through what it would have been like to have ridden up to the second floor in that elevator? *Not* to have done it, but to have walked up the stairway and stood in front of the closed elevator door and honestly, carefully, intelligently thought through what it would have been like to have ridden up and stepped out of the elevator?

Subject: Oh, I can ride elevators, but I can't ride with too many people or for too many floors. If I'm going to the sixth floor, I have to break it up into two trips by getting off at the third floor.

Erickson: But I still asked you a question you haven't answered.

Subject: I never thought of it.

Erickson: Don't you think that would be an awfully good question to think about, and then walk up to the third floor and honestly, sincerely, objectively, intellectually think through the entire process. Take one flight at a time, really thinking it through, without ever challenging yourself, without ever forcing yourself. Just go through a complete, objective, intellectual examination of the opportunity of taking in some subjective feelings. Then repeat the process with one person in the elevator with you, but still walking up and standing by the door and thinking it through. Then repeat the whole process and think it through with three, four, five, six, seven, eight, nine people. Is it worth your while, worth your time, worth your effort?

Subject: I am willing to try anything.

Erickson: Not anything—you know that. You are not willing to try anything, let's face that fact right away. You just aren't willing to face *anything*. Therefore, let's face the things you can face comfortably and safely.

Subject: There is no problem from the first to the second floor. There is no problem going from the second to the third floor.

Erickson: There is a problem thinking it through and really understanding what it must have been like to have been in an elevator and all the feelings that you could have had; all the feelings you could have had with one, two, three, four, five, six people, and with two dozen people! All the feelings you could have had in traveling in an elevator from the first floor to the sixth, to the twelfth, to the twentieth.

You see, a person with a phobia doesn't really like to think about his own fears. He likes to keep away from then. I think he should keep away from them, but I think he'd better recognize what a safe distance is. Standing outside a closed elevator door is a very safe distance *to be free to think without doing.* There is too much confusion in the phobic person's mind about thinking and doing. He confuses doing with thinking. He confuses objective thinking with subjective thinking. Every time you get the phobic person to be completely objective in his thinking and not to do things, and not to confuse thinking with doing, then he has a chance to examine things.

Now, in the matter of using hypnosis with you, I think the best use of hypnosis with you is this: That you be willing to learn hypnosis not as a therapeutic measure at all, but to learn hypnosis as a measure of being free and easy and relaxed and comfortable in your own chosen chair in the privacy of your own apartment, your own home, where you are comfortable and where you go into a trance. Whether it be by suggestion of your therapist or at your own suggestion, go into a trance and see if you can learn what objective thinking is; see if you can learn to differentiate between *objective thinking* and *doing.*

Certainly, there is no elevator around here. Certainly, I am not going to push you into any elevator of any sort. I am not going to do anything to you except to ask you to examine mentally, intellectually, certain of your own body feelings.

Exploring Sensations, Perceptions, and Thinking in Phobias

Erickson: I would like to tell you to close your eyes . . . . Close them now. All right, now you have your eyes closed. You know that you are in a room of a certain size. You know that other people are here. You know that you are sitting with your legs crossed and your hands together. You know that I am talking to you. Have you really examined the feelings in your eyelids and your eyeballs?
Subject: Yes.
Erickson: What part of it have you noticed?
Subject: I can feel my lids closed.
Erickson: What else do you feel?
Subject: My hands together.
Erickson: What about your eyelids?
Subject: Just that they are closed.
Erickson: Just that they are closed. Yet the doctor is sitting beside you; I am sitting beside you. But you notice the quivers.
Subject: I notice that, too.
Erickson: They are your eyelid quivers. The doctors are sitting beside you; I am sitting beside you; but you notice quivers. Why didn't you tell me?
Subject: I didn't notice it before.
Erickson: You had your power of sensation, and you had your attention directed to your eyes. Now I would like to have you notice something else.

There are certain sounds in this room. From earliest childhood, we learn to recognize sounds to the right and sounds to the left, front to the back, up and down, from the near, from the far. We tend to localize sounds, and when I move this way, you know I have changed my locus; when I move this way, you know I have change my position again. You can't help but know. You learn that without ever knowing that you learned it.

That is what I mean by an *objective thinking*. You ought to give attention to the feelings of your thumbs together. I suppose you think you know a lot about yourself, and I am going to ask you to answer a question verbally. Are you right-thumbed or left-thumbed?

Subject: I suppose I am right-thumbed.

Erickson: You suppose you are. Do you know?

Subject: I write with my right hand.

Erickson: All right. Put your hands above your head. Face the palms toward each other. Put them together and clasp them together. Keep them clasped and bring them down. And now tell me, without opening your eyes, which thumb is on top?

Subject: The left one.

Erickson: The dominant thumb is always on top. You have lived all these years without knowing you had a left-thumbedness. Now, how could you do that?

You know that the football couch has an awful time with that six-foot two-inch hunk of beef and bone who is all muscle, with good intelligence; who is right-armed, right-shouldered, right-eyed, right-wristed, right-handed, right-footed, and *left-hipped!* He is broken in the middle, and he can't run interference to save his soul because when he should throw his right hip, he automatically throws his left hip.

So, you are left-thumbed. How much else don't you know about yourself?

Subject: The most important things.

Erickson: The most important things. Your unconscious has that knowledge. I don't know whether you know if you are right-eyed or left-

83

eyed, but I suspect that your unconscious knows. I suspect that your dentist knows whether you are right-mouthed or left-mouthed, and I am sure you don't know. I think it is awfully important, and I think if you ask the dentist whether it's important, he'll tell you it is awfully important. People who are too predominantly right- or left-mouthed are likely to get into trouble.

That is what I mean by doing a little objective thinking about yourself, because you have been doing too much thinking about your emotions. You are afraid, but you don't know of what or why. Do you really know your relationship to the patient? You don't even know your relationship to your own thumbs. You don't know your relationship to your eyes, your mouth. You are undoubtedly right-footed in some regards; you are undoubtedly left-footed in other regards; and very few people know whether they put on their right sock first or their left sock first.

If you carry out that sort of study in psychology, you find out how uninformed psychologists are of their own behavior. Try it on medical students. They just don't know, and every woman knows how to put a belt around her own waist, but she'd better not try to put her husband's belt through the loops of his trousers!

Subject: I have the same problem.

Erickson: You have the same problem. Now, what is your relationship to space? You thought all the time that your claustrophobia was fear when it actually was ignorance of space and your relationship to space. How do sounds appear to you when the wall is close and when the wall is far away from you? What do you do with a blind patient who hasn't dared to leave the house and walk around the block for ten years? You teach him to stand on the corner, and stand there and stand there. You usually pick out a filling station where there is a kindly man standing there, and when a car comes in, you ask the blind person to listen to that car. When it drives away, the station attendant comes over and tells him it was a Ford pickup; and pretty soon that blind man can tell you a Ford pickup is coming down the street long before the station man can identify it by sight. The blind man learns something about space. When my blind friend, Danny, was taught how to hear space, he decided to walk around the city of Phoenix to find out all the different kinds of noises there were, and how far away from the streets some of the buildings were, and how close to the street some of the buildings were.

Subject: He did not have a choice, though.

Erickson: Have you?

Subject: Yes.

Erickson: What is your choice?

Subject: I can walk upstairs or stay out of phobic places. The blind man did not have a choice—he had to adapt himself.

Erickson: I didn't ask Danny to adapt himself. I just asked him to *learn* something about noises. If I had tried to tell Danny, "I am going to teach you how to walk around the city of Phoenix," Danny would have ceased to be my patient. But Danny was willing to learn to recognize noises, and that was all that was necessary. Then he started measuring space and perceiving its quality.

Danny held a five-year contract in Las Vegas as a pianist, and that is a long time to hold a contract in Las Vegas. I taught him to recognize noises. Danny, standing there safely on the sidewalk, was really studying the noise of the traffic—not *doing* a thing about the traffic, not trying to walk. Just within his own mind, he was calmly thinking and wondering about the noises he heard.

Do you want to bother about your fear? Or

would you really like to learn something about space and the sounds in space?

Subject: If it's related to my fear, I wouldn't.

Erickson: Are you in a position to bargain?

Subject: Not really.

Erickson: Not really. Not really. Therefore, one doesn't bargain, because if you learn space and sound, you can't fear—just as Danny couldn't fear when he learned space and sound. I didn't try to treat Danny for his agoraphobia.

I mentioned to you the scientist who came to see me. He did the most beautiful bit of objective thinking you could ever imagine. He described for me exactly what the upper berth of a Pullman car could be like. He was willing to speculate on the number of inches wide and long, and how much time it would take to exhaust the air in normal breathing. He did a great deal of thinking about that. Then the question arose concerning a transatlantic flight: How much air is needed for the passengers?

The result of it was that he lost his claustrophobia without even trying. He could speculate on how long sound takes to go from here to the wall, and bounce back from the wall, and bounce back from any boards to the wall, and so on. He could speculate on how long it would take the airways to dissipate; and he could reduce that speculation to a mathematical formula. The interviews with me were looked upon as charming mathematical exercises. All I asked of him was objective thinking, and I didn't try to cure his fears.

You want your phobia cured. I think you'd better let your phobia *lessen.* I'm not going to stop you. In its place, you put more and more and more objective thinking, not as a curative measure but as a scientific measure—the way that particular scientist did. He challenged me to propose any area of space, any shape, that he couldn't reduce to a mathematical formula. He challenged me in the matter of sound waves, and we had a delightful time.

Fear, Control, and Emotions in Phobias

Subject: I realize you are not going to run out of air. It's something you don't have control over. But if it's something that you rely on yourself and not other people—then everything is all right.

Erickson: You say you haven't got control. You have enough control to use it all the time.

Subject: I mean if I were operating the elevator, and if I had control of all electricity, then I wouldn't mind going up and down, because I could stop it when I wanted to. Same thing with driving. If I don't have to delegate responsibility to someone else, I don't have any problem.

Erickson: But you are still talking about your emotional reactions. It is always your emotional reactions that concern you. What else is there in your phobia besides emotional reaction?

Subject: That's it—there is nothing besides an emotional reaction.

Erickson: There isn't?

Subject: Not that I can find.

Erickson: Not that you can find.

Subject: It's all emotion.

Erickson: That is what you experience.

Subject: That's right.

Erickson: But is there anything else that you can experience? You can believe implicitly and tell everybody you know that you are right-thumbed, and then find out that you are left-thumbed. There is another side of the story.

Subject: I could be wrong.

Erickson: You would be wrong if you thought your problem was all emotional.

Subject: It can't be physical because there is plenty

of air, and there is an escape hatch at the top of the elevator.

Erickson: But when you think of the escape hatch, you are thinking of movement in terms of fear and escape.

Subject: That's true.

Erickson: But you are not thinking in terms of *more space.*

Subject: Not rationalizing.

Erickson: Is it rationalizing when you say this room is so long? Or is that stating a fact?

Subject: It's what I noticed.

Erickson: The number of inches is a scientific fact, too. So there is more to it than just fear. You add to your fear a knowledge of certain scientific facts—the number of exits, for example. But you still think about it in terms of fear.

I have spent this time with you to illustrate to the group that in handling certain types of patients, the patient's first task is to learn that he has a symptom that occupies all of his attention, and he doesn't know what else there is that exists. Fear does not exist in a vacuum; it exists *in relationship* to realities of some kind: to realities of an objective kind or to realities of a subjective kind. But they *are* realities. The patient who is phobic tends to look upon just one aspect of his emotion.

You had better find out some of the other things you have overlooked in examining the patient. As a phobic patient yourself, I can assure you that you can find a reason—many reasons—that you never thought of, that are really connected with your fear. I don't believe you really know what you are afraid of. You have an overwhelming fear, and it isn't a matter of control. It is not just a matter of space; it is not a matter of people; it is not a matter of distance. I wonder what your fear is. You ought to wonder, too.

Subject: I do. If I could understand it, maybe I could do something about it.

Erickson: Can you understand the fear if you isolate it from all relationships?

Subject: No.

Erickson: That is what you are doing.

Subject: I try not to. I try to think of examples: If my hands were tied behind my back, and there was plenty of air, why should I get panic-stricken?

Erickson: Wouldn't it be just as easy to think about yourself in a plane with your hands resting comfortably in your lap? Why do you have to tie your hands behind you? That is unreasonable and unreal.

Subject: It's much more of a restriction.

Erickson: Do you have to think about restriction?

Subject: Being in an elevator is restriction. It's a small room.

Erickson: Is it really a restriction?

Subject: You can't get out unless you open the door.

Erickson: Do you suppose that statement is correct?

Subject: I think it is.

Erickson: I have known many a small room that had an open door that didn't have to be opened. So you are misstating that room, right then and there. Right?

Subject: I don't quite understand you.

Erickson: Does every small room have to have all the doors closed? Couldn't a room be very small and still have the door wide open?

Subject: Yes.

Erickson: That is right. And couldn't a very large room have every door closed?

Subject: It would be all right as long as I could open them.

Erickson: As long as *you* could open them. What makes you so important that you think you are the only person who could open the doors? I have been in a cell block—a very large cell block—and the turn-key stood outside, and the guard opened the door. Is that any reason to have a phobia about it?

Subject: I don't know.

Erickson: How far do you want to go in discovering how much is fear and how much is fact?

Subject: It depends on—

Erickson: It can't depend on anything except your desire.

Subject: It would be the same as throwing someone in the water who didn't know how to swim.

Erickson: How would that be comparable?

Subject: He might drown, or he might learn to swim. To put him in an elevator, he might hurt someone or possibly go insane.

Erickson: Want to bet on it?

Subject: No.

Erickson: You don't believe in yourself?

Subject: No.

Erickson: Then you don't believe in what you tell me. You don't believe you'd go insane. You don't think you'd commit murder.

Subject: I don't know—it's an unknown. I wouldn't want to take the chance.

Erickson: Well, I suggest you get in the elevator with Sonny Liston or Cassius Clay!

Subject: I am not a hero.

Erickson: I don't think you would kill either one of them. That rather rules out the question of murder, doesn't it?

Subject: Well, I would go the other way, probably—perhaps. Of course, I don't know. It's just what you feel would happen.

Erickson: You are still dealing with emotion, just now, not thought.

Subject: It's emotion.

Erickson: Let's keep it clear in your mind. *That's*

emotion, not that. Let's talk about it as an emotional problem.

I have taken this time with you because the first approach made to the phobic patient has to be at this utterly wrong intellectual level, because that is what the patient always insists upon. Sooner or later he gets tired of it. Sooner or later you will have an opportunity to see where to penetrate the wall of emotion with which he has surrounded himself. Then, once you have discovered that, you can deal with it.

Subject: Deal with it in one way? If someone else in some elevator has some problem —

Erickson: It can be dealt with.

Subject: In that respect, yes. If someone else is in a bad way—yes, I have helped other people because I feel the same way they do and I know how to help them.

Erickson: And once you discover that, you can compete with them.

Subject: I never thought about it in that way.

Erickson: Well, thanks very much for coming up. You've got a lot of thinking to do.

Your first contact with phobic patients is essentially a contest. They have been contesting a fear for a very, very long time. They have come to you with certain incontrovertible feelings. They believe implicitly that there is no intellectual approach to the problem. Once they bear in mind that there is another way of thinking about it, they have made that very minute adjustment to the fact that there might possibly be another way of dealing with their problem—however remote the possibility. Then you circle around their defenses and their fears and their anxieties, and you try to build up a situation in which you can deal with them at a purely emotional level.

Phobic patients have got to bear in mind one important thing: that *you* have no fear of that particular phobia they have. Every phobic patient I have encountered has had in the back of his or her mind that I, too, must have within my system a hidden phobia, a fear; and they really try to convince themselves that I've got it.

So the first thing I try to do is to let them discover that I really haven't got that phobia. I don't try to tell them that I've got acrophobia or some other phobia. I let them know I don't have any particular phobia so that they feel a kinship with me at that particular emotional level.

Why do phobic patients come into therapy? They want some sort of an emotional relationship, and you deny them that experience by reducing the first interview to an intellectual contest. If they come back to you, they are going to seek from you some evidence of some emotional kinship.

What did that scientist do? He really hunted around in the field of science to see in what field of science we could have a kinship. He talked about some stratospheric stuff I can't even remember, and he talked about the aurora borealis in terms I could not understand, and finally he came down to the question of mathematics. I could understand a few things in the field of mathematics, and I could talk to him of my very young son who was interested in mathematics. Then the entire course of therapy developed along that line, along that tenuous emotional relationship in the field of mathematics.

But it started out with that very nice intellectual contest. Fortunately, he wanted to build up some emotional kinship, but he picked a lot of different scientific fields in which I was uninformed before he picked mathematics. I knew what he was doing, and so I was very careful to make him struggle harder and harder, and to not disclose that I did know certain things about various subjects. When he came to mathematics, I felt I did know enough to be at least an amateur, and he could be my instructor in that, and that established a very nice relationship.

Therapy didn't take very long, because he promptly started to reduce his phobia to a mathematical phobia. He began thinking about it objectively, and then a lot of emotional background which had nothing to do with his phobia came out to the foreground, and spatial relationships had nothing to do with actual space. A space was the distance between himself and his wife in so many different things. It wasn't really space after all. It was the alien character of their different individual interests, which he had reduced to space and agoraphobia.

Rossi: It is difficult to appreciate and assess this long passage showing Erickson's approach to certain phobic patients, because it is so different from traditional theory and practice. It has been included in this volume to illustrate Erickson's belief that the source of the phobia was due to a restriction in sensations, perceptions, and thinking in patients who were essentially caught in cul-de-sacs of emotions. This demonstration illustrates the extremely detailed type of exploration that Erickson pursued into the sensory-perceptual dynamics of emotional processes. It reminds us of his own struggle as a wounded healer to learn how to deal with his sensory-perceptual disorders and illnesses.

PART II

Facilitating Inner Work Through "Manipulation"?

Parental Resistance to Facing the Truth

Utilizing Resistance to Obtain Information,
Focus Attention, and Elicit Self-Responsibility:
The "Unncessary" Four-Hour Interview

I have been asked to discuss this matter of resistant patients. Whatever your patient brings into your office is part of his problem. You can usually discuss the behavior in terms of a manifestation of resistance, but it is still a part of the patient's problem.

I can think of the physician who was in my office on Wednesday. He has been to my workshops; he has read many of my publications. He wanted to see me about his son. He and his wife told me all about their son. But I didn't like the story they told me—it seemed so utterly inadequate and completely uninformative. I questioned them and questioned them and questioned them, but they simply did not tell me the things I thought were necessary to know.

Then I interviewed the son. It didn't take long to recognize the son's problem, and I made very sure that I knew exactly what his problem was.

Then I interviewed the father and mother again for another hour. The father is trained in law and medicine. He has his medical degree; he has a speciality degree; and he has a good background in psychiatry as well.

I interviewed the son once more, and then I interviewed the father for yet another hour. Still he did not disclose any information that could give me the slightest hint as to the nature of his son's problems. It was beginning to seem possible that he might not know what the problem was! The question for me became, should I break the news to him in such a fashion that he would have to face the fact? I again quizzed the father and mother together: Did they really want to know what was wrong with their son? Since they have a 14-year-old daughter in addition to the 18-year-old son, I thought I'd better make them face the fact.

I called the son in, and in the presence of his parents I blew the son up into a perfectly beautiful pre-schizophrenic manifestation—a completely unmistakable pre-schizophrenic manifestation. I sent the son back out into the waiting room, whereupon the father said: "You know, I have been discussing the fact with the boy's mother that he may be schizophrenic."

Now this man had not once hinted that he had that amount of understanding or insight. He was going to make me prove it the hard way. Why did he waste four hours of my time by making me build up the situation in that fashion? I could have triggered the schizophrenic episode during the first hour. Why did the father waste all of that time with his own resistance? Was he desperately hoping that I couldn't possibly diagnose schizophrenia, or potential schizophrenia, in that boy? The illness was there, and the father knew it. He had suspected it very strongly for several years. That resistance in the father made the father just as much a patient as was his son!

I then raised the question: "Are you going to wait until your 14-year-old daughter is 18 years old before you bring her to me or to some other psychiatrist? Or do you want her treated now? Father looked at Mother, and Mother looked at Father. "Next year," they answered. Resistance! Next year will be fine," I replied, "but what about this year, or the year after next year?" *I was placing the burden of responsibility fully upon them.* Finally, the mother's conclusion was: "You know, the sooner the better." Now that is what I thought, too! The sooner the better. When I made that statement, ". . . or the year after next year," they recognized the absurdity of any further delay.

You take resistance and you wonder in what fashion you can maneuver it, in what fashion you can manipulate it, in what fashion you can utilize it to get the patient to do some intelligent thinking about the problem at hand. I can assure you that inwardly I was rather annoyed that a physician with that amount of training avoided giving me the information. But I knew that it was also important for me to discover the nature and character of the father's personality. If I am to treat the son, I'd better know what kind of a father he has; I'd better know what kind of a mother he has; I'd better know who dominates in that household. Four hours spent, yes. I could have gotten that information within 15 minutes' time if the father had cooperated, but it wouldn't have helped me to understand in a thorough way the circumstances in which that 18-year-old boy lives. If I'm going to do any kind of therapy, I'd better understand the father, I'd better understand the mother, I'd better have an exceedingly clear picture of them. All in all, I think the four hours were well spent—in spite of the fact that I knew they could have given me the information inside of 15 minutes.

Rossi: Herein we find as clear a statement as we could hope for in illuminating how Erickson understood the equivalent use of the words *manipulate, maneuver,* and *utilize.* His maneuvering and manipulation were directed toward stimulating the father to "do some intelligent thinking about the problem at hand." That is, Erickson was using his *interpersonal* "manipulative" skills to motivate the father to do his own *intrapersonal* inner work. This was Erickson's way of placing the burden of therapeutic change on the father's own intrapersonal processes: by utilizing those very processes to facilitate problem resolution created in the father's own unique way. This interpretation of Erickson's way of "manipulating" is confirmed by his latter statement, "I was placing the burden of responsibility fully upon them."

Erickson's use of "manipulation" to facilitate the patient's inner creation of his own solutions is thus very different from the more directive, authoritarian, and naive use of manipulation to program, control, and direct the patient's outer behavior along preconceived lines.

Resistance and Defense

Depotentiating Resistance to Trance: Stopping Smoking: Trance Induction via Questions, Not Knowing, and the Negative: Trance without Awareness of It: Time Distortion and the "Secret Cure"

Why do you interview your patients? To get information. When patients show a great deal of resistance, bear in mind that the more resistance they show you, the more informative they actually are going to be. This means that they will disclose more of their weaknesses to you. You ought to regard their weaknesses and resistances as their defenses in various directions. We never defend ourselves unless we hurt somewhere. So you need to know where your patient hurts, and how much he hurts; because he is going to put up defenses against the hurt, and those defenses are best recognized as resistances.

What do you do about resistance? Do you feel defeated and helpless in its face? I can give you an excellent technique for handling resistance in a good number of cases. Take the patient who says: "I have been to all of your friends. Some of them worked on me for 30 hours to induce a hypnotic trance, but they all failed. So I have come to Phoenix to have you fail, too."

I think I'd better recognize right away that I am not going to enter into a contest with that patient. I'd better recognize that I am going to lose if I try to struggle with that patient, because that patient can out-struggle me. I think the approach I ought to take is the following:

"You went to these other friends of mine, these other therapists. Why? For what reason?"

"I have emphysema," the patient replied. "I've got worries about my heart condition and my blood pressure; I smoke four packs of cigarettes a day, and I think something ought to be done."

Now that is something I can agree with, right then and there. So I said: "Something really ought to be done, and what do you think really ought to be done? Now where is the burden of responsibility? What do you really think ought to be done?" I am not arguing with the patient. *I am asking for information, but I put a question into the patient's mind without her realizing that I had forcibly thrust it into her awareness.* I continued:

"Yes, you persisted with all four of my friends. Now how do you think I should help you in this particular regard? You went to them for hypnosis. Did you come to me for hypnosis? Did you come to have me fail to induce hypnosis? Or did you come thoroughly in regard to your emphysema, in regard to your smoking?

"Now, I would like to have your attention. I *don't* want you looking at my bookcase over there. You *don't* need to count the number of books on the shelf, or to read the titles; you don't need to look at the filing cabinet there; you *don't* need to look at the clutter on my desk; you *don't* need to look at the pictures, or at anything else. You came here to find out whether or not I can give you some help. Why *don't* you look at that clock there on my desk? That will hold your eyeballs still. And if you hold your eyeballs still, you can hold your head still; and if you hold your ears still, you can give me your attention so that I can discuss your emphysema, your cardiac condition. I can ask you questions, and you can answer so that I gain a better understanding of you. I can talk to you about cigarettes, and I can ask you questions about your smoking. And you can look at that clock and hold your eyeballs still, hold your head still, hold your ears still.

"And you can listen to me with your conscious mind while your attention wanders; you can do some conscious thinking about the planes overhead, or the street noises, or the birds outside the window, or the secretary typing out in the other room. All of that is unimportant, as far as I am concerned. The important thing is the medical consideration; that is what I am concerned about. I am not concerned about the secretary, the birds, the planes, the street noises. They are all unimportant, but if your conscious mind wants to wander, go ahead, let it. *You don't need to go into a trance.* All I want is the full attention of your unconscious mind, which goes everywhere with you. It came into the office with you; it is within six feet of me, and it is listening to me right now. And while you are looking at that clock, *your unconscious mind is listening to me whether or not you know it*—but I think you know it." (I saw her head nodding)

Yes, her unconscious mind was listening. What more did I need in the way of hypnosis than to have her unconscious mind listening? And her unconscious head nodding told me, "Yes, I am listening to you." My communication is with her unconscious mind, so I had what I needed. And how deep a trance do you need with a resistant patient? Too many resistant patients make this matter of trance induction a contest between you and them. I think you ought to avoid that as much as possible. Your problem of therapy is what matters. I never did try to put the emphysema patient in a trance. All I wanted her to do was to let her conscious mind roam at will in its thinking; to pay attention to its random thoughts, to outside noises, or to anything that it wanted to give attention to. At the same time I wanted her unconscious mind, which was only six feet away from me, to listen.

She had a two-hour appointment, and she had anticipated a two-hour struggle between the two of us. When I finished my discussion with her unconscious mind, I told her the time of her appointment for the next day (she had told me that she wanted a two-hour appointment every day for a week). She replied, "But I have been here only 10 minutes!" I replied, "You'd better look at the clock. You know you came here at two o'clock, and it's four o'clock now." She looked at her watch; she listened to her watch—it was running just fine. She looked at my watch. Somehow or other it was four o'clock, but she had come in just 10 minutes ago! I explained, "You know, when you listen intently to something, you don't really pay attention to the passage of time."

Why should I tell her that she had been in a trance? There was no sense in telling her. When you are really listening to something—when you are really listening to ideas that you can understand and that are meaningful to you—you are not going to watch the minute-hand of the clock.

My work with this woman occurred several years ago. I recently spoke with her, and her statement was: "My emphysema has very much improved; my blood pressure is down to normal; my compulsions about smoking are gone; and I am really enjoying life. I have often wondered what became of the time I spent in your office. I have a sneaking suspicion that I went into a trance."

My reply was: "What is important about your visit to my office? Did you derive the benefit that you wanted? Shall we take up the issue of whether you did or didn't go into a trance? Or shall we take up the really important issue of, did you derive the desired medical benefit?"

Her reply was: "The medical benefit is all that is important."

Why shouldn't we leave it on that basis? *Human nature likes secrets.* Your best way of dealing with small children is to tell them secrets. And small children grow up into small-children-grown-older-and-taller, and that is all. You'd better recognize that your patients require the same, earnest, respectful liking that you have for little children.

> *Rossi:* In this trance induction Erickson helps the patient shift her attention from her resistance and defensiveness to her very real concern about her emphysema and her need to stop smoking. Erickson's use of a striking series of negatives (*don't*) in the beginning of the induction is an example of his penchant for taking over the patient's negative attitudes (defenses and resistances), while at the same time giving her something simple and positive to facilitate the experience of "non-doing" so essential for the initial phase of trance induction.'

Erickson's statement—"I am asking for information, but I put the question into the patient's mind without her realizing that I had forcibly thrust it into her awareness"—provides us with another dramatic revelation of his indirect method: *he evokes the patient's inner processes in a manner that places the burden of therapeutic change "forcibly" yet indirectly within the patient.*

"Trance without awareness of it" seems to well describe the situation wherein the patient does not consciously recognize she was in trance, yet she experiences a striking time distortion that is characteristic of altered states of high absorption.

Erickson's interesting comment on the use of secrets is something he frequently mentioned in conversation but did not discuss in writing. Secrets contain a profound truism about the way human nature works. Most things in life happen without our awareness: our heartbeat and the functions of most biological processes, the automatic functioning of the unconscous mind, our many habit patterns, and so forth. Erickson presumes to utilize all these natural ways of development, being, and change when he facilitates therapeutic goals without the patient knowing exactly how or why the therapy was effective.

Therapeutic Attitudes toward Resistant Patients

Communicating Competence, Confidence, and Fallibility: Making Deliberate Mistakes

I have given you a particular kind of technique in detail because I think you ought to view any resistance manifested by a patient as a part of the problem. And what is your most courteous way of dealing with that resistance? If you are lenient in any way— if you pretend patients aren't being resistant—just exactly what kind of respect will they have for you? Confronting resistance can present a rather difficult situation for you as a person. The medical patient is told: "This tooth is really a rather painful tooth for you. . . . This broken arm is a rather painful arm . . . . This neurodermatitis is a rather itchy sort of thing." I think you had better recognize that this matter of interpersonal relationship is also a rather painful, itchy, troublesome, aching sort of thing. Once you and your patients understand that, you can dispense with any sense of fear, any sense of worry.

You ought to have an attitude of confidence in your own medical ability. Why shouldn't you? You certainly are better trained than your patients. Your patients come to you because they think that you are better trained than they—that you know more than they know. That doctor who gave me such a hard time didn't come to me because he thought he knew *more* than I did. He came to me determined to make me prove that *I knew a lot more than he did;* determined to make me prove that I could find out things, no matter how deeply buried or how deeply concealed they were. He expected me to know more than he did, but he wanted me to prove it undeniably.

Patients come to you because they respect you, and because they expect something of you. I think your attitude ought to be one of utter expectancy that your patients are going to benefit from your knowledge. I think your attitude toward your resistant patients ought to be marked by utter and absolute confidence in your ability to do things, to think clearly, and to convey understandings. Above all, I want to impress upon you the tremendous importance of never trying to be omnipotent with any patient. *I deliberately and intentionally make mistakes so that my patients can correct me.* Why should I put a halo around my head? Why should I create a mysterious aura? I want my patients to recognize that I am just another human being, for as soon as they recognize that, then they can communicate with me. I can think of all the "stuffed shirts" whom my patients have described to me. Instead of establishing a good rapport with their patients, these stuffed-shirt therapists spend their time attempting to impress their patients with their importance. This doesn't get anybody very far.

One of the techniques I like to use with resistant patients is to simply say: "Let's see. This is July 14th, isn't it? No, it isn't." Then I look at the calendar, and they see me correcting the date. I have to look at a calendar. They do not want me to be all-knowing. They merely want me to be competent in my medical knowledge; they want me to be confident in my attitude toward them, but not omnipotent in regard to unimportant things such as the day of the week, the date of the month, and so forth. In other words, you let patients see that you do have weaknesses. Why do resistant patients show so much resistance? They want to find out how human you really are, and I think it's a good idea to accommodate them.

Therapist Vulnerability; Patients' Attacks

Utilizing Apparently Casual Conversation to Depotentiate Resistance; The Importance of Effective Phrasing; Handling Verbal Attacks via Personal Admissions

I can recall the alcoholic who came to me with a hostile, antagonistic look on his face. My immediate statement to him was, "I was somewhat younger than you when I got thoroughly drunk for the first time." He looked at me with a disgusted expression on his face. He knew immediately that I wasn't going to take a sanctimonious attitude toward his alcoholism, and he knew that I knew something about being drunk. And I told him where it was I got drunk and in whose company; and he listened with a great deal of interest. Then there was that beautiful air of alcoholic resistance that he manifested toward me, but he manifested it toward me as a physician to whom he could talk. His hostility quickly evaporated.

I think it is awfully important for you to speculate over and over again on how you could have better carried out that little casual conversation with each resistant patient you encounter. You make a few minor remarks—but those remarks can carry a great deal of significance to the individual. After you have interviewed the patient, you look up your case history to analyze and reflect on the meaningfulness of your notes in relation to the patient's own personality. Then you wonder how you could have better phrased this remark or that remark. Why have any hurt feelings?

I can think of the patient who said to me, "That is an awfully clumsy limp you have." My reply was: "I know how clumsy my limp is—much better than you do. I hope you never find out how really clumsy it is. You ought to see me on ground that is rough, if you want to appreciate how clumsy I can really be." The patient had said something intended to offend me. Well, I'd better recognize the fact that I am clumsy. And I'd better point out that I am clumsier on rough ground than I am on a smooth floor. It is the same principle as admitting that my hair is gray and that I wear glasses. Why not? What is wrong? There is your willingness to accept an attack by a patient. He wants to find out just how vulnerable you are. That is part of his resistance. How vulnerable are you to any attack he makes by way of expressing that resistance?

QUESTIONS AND ANSWERS

Reframing Symptoms

Treating Ulcerative Colitis via Contingent Suggestions
Establishing Respect for Organ-Body Language:
Colitis as "Marvelous Colon Dexterity"

Audience Member: How do you treat an ulcerative colitis patient?

Erickson: One of the first things I would tell a patient suffering from ulcerative colitis is this: "For a long time now you have suffered from ulcerative colitis. It is painful, it is disagreeable, it is troublesome. In all the time you have suffered from this affliction, I really don't think that you have been able to give an honest-to-goodness, earnest respect to your colon. You know, your colon is really a marvelous construction. I would like to have you think about it as something that is of marvelous construction. The human hand is one of the most important things in the development of civilization. It is very dexterous. It can do the most intricate work. But can you imagine being able to combine the hands in any position you want? Yet your colon can do that. It is a rather delicate mechanism. Now let us give some sort of respect to your colon. *As you develop a respect for your colon, you are not going to have the tension, the anxiety, the fear; you are going to take a much better attitude toward your colon, and you are going to give your colon an opportunity to get over its ulceration.*"

This redoing of the patient's tense and anxious attitude toward his ulcerative colitis is a tremendously important step in correcting the condition. You teach the patient to respect, genuinely, his colon. I think you should. It is so very, very important that all of us respect every organ in our body.

I can tell the patient who comes into my office with a mouthful of snags: "You really ought to respect those teeth; you really ought to respect your appetite; you really ought to respect your stomach. Now I am not a dentist, and I am not going to take any teeth from you. But I am going to urge you to develop a wholehearted respect for your body." I have sent many a patient to a dentist by just building up that concept of body respect, organ respect, respect for one's general health. Ulcerative colitis is the same sort of problem.

The Nature of Defense Mechanisms

Relationship between Hypnotizability and Ego Defenses?;
Symptoms as Interpersonal Maneuvers

Audience Member: Is it correct to assume from what you just said that a person's resistance to hypnosis is correlated with his ego defenses? That is, do his ego defenses determine his hypnotizability?

Erickson: In the first place, *ego* is a theoretical concept that is very, very useful and convenient for formulating ideas. However, I don't think it should be regarded as a reality. What are defenses to the patient? Defenses are personality reactions to the situation in which the patient finds himself. It isn't just his ego, or his superego, or his id that is present. He's got defenses that relate to all three of those concepts; defenses that relate to his total personality. What are his defenses? I really don't know if his defenses relate to me. I do know that his defenses relate to his understanding of hypnosis, to his expectation of what I am going to do, to his attitude toward his own illness.

How many of you would want me to take away all of your migraine headache? Probably none of you. A migraine headache is very, very valuable, and you may want to put it to good use sometime. For example, say you want a new fur coat but your husband is a tight-wad. Having that migraine headache just when you want that fur coat could be very, very important to your husband. You can be disappointed in a most tactful fashion, and he is going to bring that fur coat home to you—just to have his own way. People know about such maneuvers.

What about the small child who says: "Mommy is going to scold me if she finds this out. I'd better develop an ache in my foot when I tell her about this—that will ameliorate the situation tremendously." And that child is right. (Erickson now tells an anecdote about a bassett dog walking with his master. The dog got the master to do his bidding by affecting a limp in his hind leg!)

Stuttering

Treatment via Re-education, Not Control

Audience Member: [Question concerns the control of stuttering]

Erickson: How do you control the situation? You don't. You point out to the stutterer tactfully and gently that speech is something that is learned. It can be learned the right way, it can be learned the wrong way. You point out that many a stutterer can learn a foreign language without stuttering. What kind of an approach are you going to take in regard to this emotional language that was learned in the wrong way? There are many different techniques. Alexander has his patients learn how to talk freely and comfortably in the trance state, and then he transfers that ability, bit by bit, to the ordinary waking state. Most of us learned to talk by uttering meaningless sounds and then putting the sounds together. As we learned to put the sounds together, we learned free and easy speech. But to ask a person to control something that years of experience has taught him he cannot control is to walk into a trap. [2]

Of Beards and Roses

Behavior Problems of Children and Parents

Audience Member: I know of an 18-year-old boy who is growing a beard. He is a good-looking boy without a beard, but he is driving his mother out of her mind by insisting on having that beard. A contest is now going on between the two of them as to whether his beard should come off. Do you have any suggestions?

Erickson: The mother is definitely going to lose the contest! The mother is the patient, not the boy. And you are going to have a difficult patient in that mother, for you need to teach her how to respect a growing boy's needs and wishes and ambitions. Then you ought to talk to the boy, gently and carefully pointing out that he really doesn't have to prove his manhood with a beard. There are dozens of other ways to prove one's manhood that are much more interesting. He does not have to show off his manhood, and he does not have to defy his mother. How on earth can he expect his mother to understand? She is a woman, with a woman's thinking and a woman's feelings. She hasn't the slightest idea how a beard feels on the face. How could he really expect her to understand the joy and comfort of a beard? Since she cannot understand it, why contest with her?

You see, a mother who wants to fight with her son over the issue of growing a beard is probably still treating him like a baby. How much tendency does she have to butter his toast— as if he couldn't butter it all by himself? You will find in many similar cases that the mother is doing a whole lot of things that burn up Sonny. The mother anticipates the son's every move, and she doesn't let him do the things he would really like to do. It has often amused me to see parents buttering toast for their grown-up children, and to see the expressions on the grown-up children's faces. You know, you could sour the sweetest of milk with those expressions!

Audience Member: I am treating a boy from a medical family who was arrested for pulling out rosebushes in a large suburban area in the middle of the night. Do you see any meaning in this behavior?

Erickson: My suspicion is that the parents have been trying to force that kid to develop a liking for gardening. That is just a suspicion. They are trying to inculcate in him some kind of an appreciation for flowers, or roses, or something of that sort. Or, it may be that his girlfriend's name is Rose, and the mother is trying to tell her son that he must stop dating her. So he is getting rid of one Rose, but going out to pick up another rose! I don't really know what is involved there.

Conveying Ideas Through Hypnosis

Grounding Textbook Concepts in
Everyday Realities: Sibling Rivalry

Hypnosis is a modality by which you convey ideas and understandings to patients. What are the ideas and understandings you want to convey? Let us take the area of psychopathology. I have read a lot of books on psychopathology, and I am going to use a rather rough example. You have all read about sibling rivalry; you have all read very beautiful discussions about sibling rivalry in textbooks. But you are not going to understand anything at all until you begin to think about the kind of sibling rivalry in that family on the other side of the tracks; and you had better think about sibling rivalry in a family of two children; in a family of eight children; in a family living in a palatial estate; in a family where Mother was an only child and Father was an only child, and they have an only child. Then you will really have to think about sibling rivalry. You encounter a problem with sibling rivalry, so you refer to your textbooks. But then you need to think about the problem in terms of everyday life. The same holds true for ego defenses, for id strivings, for superego conflicts, or whatever else you have.

Personal Experience and the Language of Biology

Using Metaphor to Facilitate
New Attitudes toward Menopause

Another topic I would like to mention briefly is this matter of talking in the language of biology. There is the woman who has had the experience of motherhood, and who is now going through the menopause. She is depressed, she is weak, she just doesn't see any purpose in life. Somehow or other you manage to get her into a sufficiently light trance so that she is able to listen, at least in part, to what you say. You begin to reminisce about the time her first baby cut his teeth, and about that awful, despairing attitude that little baby had. There was nothing but pain and distress, that he could foresee, for all the rest of his life. That is all—just the pain, distress and agony of cutting those teeth. But it was a biological process, and he went through it. He got some teeth, and he could eat some solid food. Then you raise the question to the mother: "Maybe you are cutting a certain kind of biological teeth in this menopause of yours? What do you suppose you will be like after you have completed the menopause? You are fixing teeth—biological teeth."

What have you done? You have spoken to her in the language of her own experience. You have drawn an analogy that is weighted by the love she had for that baby of hers. She is awfully concerned about her depression. But now she is going to think about her depression in terms of that little infant who was so depressed about that endless task of cutting teeth.

Indirect Suggestion

Utilizing Implication and Positive Expectancy
"Even with Resistant Subjects"

[*Approximately one page of material is deleted here due to intermittent inaudibility. Material resumes with Erickson apparently describing a demonstration induction technique used by a practitioner named Victor.*]

Victor explained that he wanted to have the task of introducing the total situation. He spent some time in a general discussion directed not anly to the gentleman on the platform, but to the entire audience, which included any others who might volunteer. Victor said something to the effect that he was going to use a technique that is useful *even with resistant subjects*. What does that mean? First, it classifies the volunteer as not resistant, and second [it establishes a positive expectancy]: if it is a technique that is successful *even with resistant subjects*, then it really ought to be very successful with a subject who isn't resistant. In other words, Victor implied success by use of his indirect suggestion.

You need to understand what to say and how to say it, so that you can imply things indirectly in an effective manner. Try to explain the technique to your patient. The explanation of the technique in your office can serve as the technique itself, because very often the patient will go into trance if you explain.

Ideomotor Signaling

Now there is something that I would like to call your attention to. I do not like to have my patients say, "Yes, I understand." I don't want them talking. In hypnosis you need to limit and restrict your patients' behavior, so you can tell them very simply: "I can understand a nodding or a shaking of the head, and while I am talking to you, you may have your eyes closed. I would like to have you show me that you can nod your head yes, or shake it no, and in that way you silently listen to me and communicate with a head nod." What patients do not realize is that restriction circumscribes their appreciation of reality. Now I don't know what you would call that technique—hand fixation, hypnomotor, or whatever. The name of the technique is always unimportant.

Temporal Considerations in Hypnosis

Conveying Confidence Indirectly; Hypnotherapists Do Not Need to Use "Challenges"

[*Erickson now comments on the demonstration apparently conducted by Dr. Irving Secter.*] During the actual use of the technique, Secter said to the subject: "You don't need to hurry; there is plenty of time." There wasn't plenty of time, but the point is that you give your patient the feeling that there is plenty of time. Don't do things too rapidly. Mean it when you say that there is plenty of time; that gives the patient a feeling that he is performing very adequately.

Secter also said, "I have confidence in you." This is a teaching situation, so he was quite direct. But in your office, your manner and the tone of your voice ought to convey that confidence indirectly. You do not use tests in your office; you merely assume very confidently that things are going well. In a teaching situation you show how tests can be applied—but the sooner you discontinue the tests and rely upon your own abilities, the better.

Rossi: By "tests" Erickson may mean the use of "challenges" ("You will not be able to open your eyes," etc.) used by authoritarian hypnotherapists of yesteryear to prove to patients that they were in trance and presumably under the control of the therapist.

112

Erickson's Observational Skills

Learning How to Recognize Trance Indicators
Manifested by Demonstration Subjects

[*Next an audience member apparently asks a question which suggests a lack of observation in regard to the preceeding demonstration. Erickson responds emphatically.*] The only comment I wish to make is this: *What on earth was the audience doing!* How many of you noted the different kinds of eyelid behavior shown by the six different subjects? How many of you noted the six different kinds of arm movement as demonstrated by those six different subjects? How many of you noted which of those subjects showed the kind of overcompensatory arm movement that occurs when a book is placed on the hand and adjustments to its weight are made? How many of you noted the lack of swallowing reflexes in some of the subjects? There was a diminution of eye-blink behavior before subjects closed their eyes. How many of you noted the time and the rate at which various subjects changed their respiratory rhythms: They all changed their respiratory rhythms, and they all did it very neatly and very adequately and very observantly. How many of you noted which subjects responded when Dr. Harron, while moving his position from one end of the platform to another, was really speaking to one specific subject? It was very, very beautiful to watch him speaking from this end of the platform, while two subjects at the other end of the platform acted as if he were standing behind them. Did you notice which two they were?

A final question: Which one of those subjects would you select, first and foremost, as an individual subject? Which subject gave you the impression that he or she would respond very, very nicely in an individual situation? Now, henceforth, listen and watch subjects carefully in order to perceive what they are really doing. Your ability to observe is awfully important in the use of hypnosis, both clinically and experimentally.

Rossi: This example of Erickson's emphasis on observation and responsiveness to the patient's behavior and body language contains a most important factor in learning how to emulate his therapeutic skills. While many have regarded Erickson as a "genius of manipulation," I have come to regard him as a "genius of observation." I recently summarized Erickson's way of teaching as follows[3]:

> . . . While it was true that Erickson's early research papers were replete with ingenious ways of manipulating people, I never saw him do anything particularly outrageous. Quite the contrary, in the last decade of his life when I studied with him, he would usually facilitate therapeutic trance only after he had observed that the patient's physical and mental processes had "quieted down." He explained that he would often tell a lot of interesting and seemingly irrelevant stories and anecdotes to "yo-yo" a person's consciousness up and down to "tire it out." Although his manner seemed casual, he was always monitoring minimal changes in the patient's emotional state by acutely observing the pulse at barely discernible spots on the face, neck, arms, or legs. He watched the patient's eyes and pupillary reflexes to see if they widened, indicating that a story had touched upon something of vital interest even before the patient had become consciously aware of it. For the most part, however, Erickson admitted that *he was utilizing those natural periods of quietness and expectation when the patient's receptivity was optimal for experiencing trance.*
>
> We soon began calling these periods of quiet receptivity the *common everyday trance* because they appeared to be a normal feature of daily life. Everyone needs to stretch a bit

and take a break every hour-and-a-half or so. A housewife staring vacantly over a cup of coffee in midmorning, a student with a faraway look in his eyes in the middle of a lecture, a truck driver who blinks in mild surprise as he suddenly reaches his destination without any memory of the last 30 minutes—all are examples of the common everyday trance.

Over the years I began compiling lists of the subtle mental and behavioral signs of the common everyday trance that Erickson was using. In my first book with Erickson, *Hypnotic Realities,* I called them "indicators of trance development." I began watching people carefully in normal daily living as well as in the consulting room to improve my observations. I gradually felt myself becoming privy to the traditional fraternity of experienced hypnotherapists who would wink and smile knowingly at one another when they spotted a colleague or person in a crowd who was drifting spontaneously into a light state of trance without quite knowing it. It was such a common observation, really, that most people did not seem to take it too seriously. It seemed to be a kind of in-group joke that only hypnotists could enjoy.

I noticed that the wisest of my senior colleagues did take these observations seriously, however. After I became adept at recognizing these mildly altered states in everyday life, I began feeling a deepening appreciation for those old yet ever new philosophical and metaphysical authors who maintained that the average person was "unawakened," "sleepwalking," "unaware of his trance condition," "lost in maya," and so forth. In some as yet unexplained manner, people really were experiencing spontaneous alterations in their consciousness in normal everyday life; they were "trancing out" without being aware of it.

I began forming a very different notion about Milton H. Erickson. While most of his colleagues liked to believe he was a "genius of manipulation and suggestion," I began to understand him more as a "genius of observation." The effectiveness of his innovative therapeutic approaches depended less on the so-called "power of suggestion" than on his ability to recognize and utilize the patient's personal life experiences and inner resources during those creative moments of the common everyday trance when they were most accessible.

In my own mind I began to substitute the word *sensitivity* for the word *suggestion*. The real source of hypnotherapeutic effectiveness was to be found in a developing sensitivity to the nuances of a patient's spontaneously shifting levels of communication between mind and body. *The secret of therapeutic transformation from illness to health and optimal states of well-being was to be realized in the utilization of a person's own repertory of inner resources during those moments of natural creativity in normal living—the common everyday trance.*

Verbal and Nonverbal Cues

Learning to Use Body and Vocal Cues for Hand Levitation

[*Some material has been lost from the original transcription; presentation resumes with Erickson commenting on demonstrations conducted by Drs. Hershman and Mann.*]

Did you notice that Hershman's hand levitation technique caused him to have a great deal of foot action on his own? There was that lifting, lifting of his shoulders, and then that

116

upping of his head. Hershman always uses his body to give expression to his words. Then he switched to a relaxation technique—the eye-fixation technique. Did you notice that then there was very, very little movement in his feet, and that his hand movements were slow and gentle and relaxed? I emphasize this not as a humorous point, but because you need to feel and sense and mean the suggestion you give to a patient. Mean it with every bit of sincerity within you. Enter into it.

If you want a patient to feel relaxed, you need to express relaxation in your voice. Mann did that in his demonstration. All you really need to do in hypnosis is to convey adequate understanding. Mann, I think, used his voice to express understanding very well, just as Hershman used his body to express the same understanding. When you enter into the process in that sort of way, you tend to time your suggestions much more adequately. You have a better measure of how long it takes to lift a finger. If you lift your foot, then you have a sensation within yourself of how rapidly your patient's finger should lift. Hershman always demonstrates that parallel lifting of the foot so that everybody can observe it. And one more thing: Did you notice that as Hershman suggested the *lifting, lifting, lifting* of the patient's hand, his voice became increasingly urgent the higher he wanted the lifting to occur?

Use your body, use your voice. Use inflection, intonation, pauses, hesitations, and subtle body cues in every possible way to convey your meaning.

Context in Treatment Approaches

The Scientific/Curious Mind of the Therapist

Yesterday I said that whatever a patient brings into the office constitutes a part of his problem. No matter what problem the patient brings you, there are always psychological and personality significances in relation to the patient's total life situation. You never consider a case without wondering about family implications, living situations, and work situations, because a patient's problem is entirely concerned with the disturbances experienced in daily living. Therefore, you ought to have an open mind—not a critical mind, not a judgmental mind—but a curious, scientific mind, wondering just what the real situation is. And so you try to appraise it. Remember that the spouse has as many rights as the patient, and you ought to respect that thoroughly. The patient can irritate the spouse thoroughly if the spouse irritates the patient. Therefore, you ought to have a comprehensive view of the total situation. That applies in dentistry as well as in psychiatry. It applies whether you are treating diabetes, psoriasis, or asthma. The asthmatic patient, after all, breathes in relationship to other people. It is very, very important that you consider what is the real situation on all fronts.

Provocation

Utilizing Anger to Motivate Recovery from a Cerebrovascular Accident[4]

I was asked to discuss a certain patient I treated who had suffered from a cerebrovascular accident. The patient had been hospitalized the entire preceeding year as a teaching case at Stanford. I didn't really go into all the medical details. I didn't really read all of the Stanford X-rays, all the neurological studies, all the this-and-that, because I was much too interested in the patient, and his wife, and the total situation. A physician friend of the patient's had seen my report on the re-education of a woman with severe brain damage[5] and had recommended that Karl be brought to me.

It was with extreme difficulty that the wife managed to get Karl into my office. Karl was aphasic; he had practically no use of his right arm; he had only restricted use of his right leg, and only restricted use of his other arm. He was horribly handicapped. Now Karl had been a very active man—he was always doing something. He had his own workshop in which he built things. As I looked at that man my feeling was, here is a very, very angry man. I think I needed to recognize that here was a very, very angry man. As I looked at his wife my feeling was, here is a very, very concerned woman. She is really concerned about her husband. Her feeling toward her husband is good, but he is just plain angry with what fate has done to him.

Now I am in a therapeutic situation. What am I going to do with a very angry man? Pacify him? He had been a teaching case at Stanford for a year, and he hadn't made any progress. He expected to live as a hopeless invalid for the rest of his life. He expected to be aphasic for the rest of his life. What kind of motivation do you give such a patient? How does one re-learn how to talk? How does one re-learn how to walk? I have a sophisticated argument that I offer patients in these kinds of handicapped situations. I explain:

"You have billions of brain cells you are never, never going to use, because you will never have the occasion to use them. You are in the habit of using a limited portion of your brain. If you want to learn to speak Chinese, and you currently only know English, you must call upon a wealth of other brain cells to learn that Chinese. And then if you want to learn Polish, you call upon still another set of brain cells."

As I looked at this particular patient, I could see his seething anger and resentment about his entire future. I didn't have the time to soothe him, I didn't have the time to pacify him. He had had a year's intensive course in building up and intensifying his anger. So (to his wife's horror) I proceeded to needle him, to irritate him, to intensify his anger. I knew what I was doing. I have had experience in using this sort of approach. I didn't do this, mind you, with my very first patients. And even when I did attempt it for the first time, I did so tentatively. But I've gained a lot of experience since I first began practice, so I simply needled him and angered him until he managed to tell me what a so-and-so I was in clear, understandable language. It delighted his wife to hear him actually articulate words. It delighted Karl to discover that he could articulate words. That is the point at which we began to build a beautiful therapeutic rapport, and that is the point at which Karl lost a good deal of his anger—because he had actually said some words.

Karl rejected his wife's offer of assistance to walk out of the office. Instead he clumsily shuffled out of the office and out of the house all by himself, requiring only a minimum of assistance to get into the car. As he left the office, Karl swore a royal oath: "I'll never come back to that so-and-so again!" His wife just laughed, she so enjoyed hearing Karl speak any words at all.

I had given him an appointment for the next day at a certain hour, but Karl went to bed stating: "I will never see that so-and-so again!" I had counseled the wife before she left my office to recall the words of Shakespeare: "Me thinks he doth protest too much." That seemed to comfort her, and she thought of it spontaneously as Karl ranted and raved in the evening. The next morning after breakfast, Karl again declared he would never, never see me. Nevertheless his wife drove the car up in front of the house, and Karl was still muttering as he limped out by himself and shuffled into the car. He also insisted on stumbling awkwardly up the steps into my office, at which point he sat down, looked me straight in the eyes, and said: "Now what are you going to do to me next?"

Karl goes swimming now. I don't know how many other things he does. He still lacks the use of one arm, but he is engaged in a variety of activities. I also taught him how to read again, because he had alexia.

Analysis of the Case

Activating Untapped Neurological Potentials: The
Therapeutic Use of Anger to Motivate Recovery

The important point for all of you to recognize is the question of how truly handicapped is the tremendously handicapped patient who comes to you? What brain cells does he have that are *unused?* You are all familiar with Lashley's research on rats running mazes. Once a rat had learned to run a maze, Lashley would destroy the part of the brain containing the learning. He would then teach the rat to use another area of its brain to learn to run the maze again. The plasticity we possess in the potential of using other areas of our brains is wonderful.

You can inspire patients with this kind of information. You suggest that they can do things, and you speak so simply and so earnestly. But you had better believe what you say. How else are you going to get a patient who is despairing to try to do things. When you convey an understanding and an earnest and sincere belief, you convey a new possibility.

Karl had been condemned to lie in bed and be a teaching case because he was paralytic, aphasic, alexic, and so on. But now Karl is going swimming, and I was informed this morning that he wants to come to Phoenix to visit me. I am going to be delighted to see that man. I don't think he has any anger left toward me. In the first place, I had no anger toward him. I stirred up his anger, and I let him realize that I stirred up his anger in order to stimulate him into activity. But I knew that as soon as he really understood what I was doing, and what he could really do, his anger would evaporate. His third visit to my office was a perfect example. He was as eager as a little child who wants to know if you have candy in the bag that you are holding. He was so delighted to come in, and so pleased to show me what he could do. He was so pleased to show me this and that, and I was so delighted to have him show me those little things. You know, a thumb movement doesn't mean much to most of you. But lie in bed paralyzed for a year and you will know what a thumb movement really means.

Audience Member: How did you stimulate his anger?

Erickson: My statement to Karl was: "What kind of an effort did you make to adjust to lying there as a teaching case? Did you appreciate the opportunity you had to offer the medical students some understanding of a helpless patient?" It wasn't a nice thing to say, but it irritated the life out of him. He just looked at me in a horrified fashion, and getting out of that chair in my office was an awful task. So he had to sit there and take it. Once his anger started to boil he became increasingly helpless, but I knew what I was doing. I knew what to say, and I knew what to continue to say.

Audience Member: Was it significant that the first words he spoke were rather violent?

Erickson: Certainly it was significant. How would you feel about being a teaching case for an entire year? How would you feel about being incapacitated for an entire year?

Vulgarity and Self-Identity

Setting an Example of Comfort to Promote Cathartic
Self-Expression in a Highly Rigid Patient:
The Need for Humanness in Professionalism

What is the teaching you received from earliest childhood? You learned that there are "charged words"; you learned to select those charged words that carry a wealth of affective meaning and to use them with the greatest of care. In the presence of the clergy, you select certain kinds of words as charged words. In the presence of an old-maid school teacher, you select other kinds of words for their charge value. In the presence of a physician, you use still other words.

When you get sufficiently angry, you simply explode. That is when the vulgarity comes out. All of us have vulgarity within us, and that includes our patients. Sometimes it is awfully, awfully useful to patients to give expression to their vulgarity. I can think of a recent patient I treated. She was an utterly stiff, painfully rigid old maid between the ages of 35 and 40. Her arms were stiff, her shoulders were stiff, her neck was stiff, her face was stiff, her legs were stiff. She had to bend painfully forward in the middle in order to sit down in a chair. She held her face straight and expressionless. It hurt just to look at her.

She answered each question I asked regarding her name, her address, her telephone number, her work, and her religious affiliations, and so forth, in a tense, painful and rigid tone of voice. I began taking the family history, but she continued to speak in that painfully rigid tone of voice that so hurt my ears.

By the third interview I brought up the matter of her gastric distress and her headaches. I myself was relaxed and comfortable, even though she was again quite rigid. I always sprawl out in my chair, because I like to be comfortable. When she came in for her fourth interview, I was sprawled out in a nice and easy stride. This time, however, *she* did the talking. With a smile on her face she said:

"I am going to do nothing but talk to you today. I have

listened to you, I have watched you. I am going to do the talking, and the first thing I am going to do is tell you about my so-and-so father who raped me when I was 10 years old." She really let loose with a tremendous tirade.

Following her tirade I said: "That is very interesting. Now, what is the next thing you want to tell me about?"

She told me about a lot of things, concluding: "I am not going to have any more headaches. I am going to live normally. I am going to tell my father—who still insists that I give him a warm and passionate kiss every time I see him—*where to go*. If I need to, I'll shove him along the way!"

There was that letting loose. Why did she finally let loose? I set an example of relaxation, of comfort, of actually enjoying her presence no matter how rigid she was. Then she herself gained a feeling of comfort in the situation.

I don't like these physicians who wear high-topped, silken hats with starched shirts and go about acting in that overly professional manner. *The therapy office is where two human beings meet to solve a problem,* and I think that you can abide by professional ethics and professional courtesy in every way and still be a human being. Patients need to know you so that they can confide in you. I think that is one of the most important points to remember.

Rossi: Erickson's use of tension, relaxation, and even vulgarity to break through rigid defenses contains much that is highly controversial. *These approaches are not for beginners!* They require a great deal of personal control, judgment, and experience on the part of the therapist. They would be best learned under careful observation, guidance, and training in professional clinics. Even with such training, use of the kinds of intrusive techniques so skillfully implemented by Erickson will never be entirely safe and therefore are not to be recommended for professional use.

The occasional effectiveness of these intrusive approaches, however, does suggest a theory concerning the therapeutic applications of slang and obscene language. In a detailed illustration and discussion of Erickson's use of sexual slang, for example, the following comments were made[6]:

This suggests the basis of an interesting new theory of the function of slang. *Slang terms* are ever-new linguistic inventions that give fresh expression to impulses in a manner that frees them from the inhibiting weight of past unfortunate associations. *Obscene terms,* on the other hand, are an aggressive attack on the listener's associative structure: obscene terms disrupt and break down the listener's attitudes and world view so that the speaker can impose his own. Slang actually begins as a delicate creative effort to express new or socially suppressed impulses. Once the slang term becomes popularized, however, it becomes so loaded with the negative associations society attaches to the referent impulse that the term becomes gross—or obscene. As an obscenity the term is then used socially for a period of time in an entirely different function: it serves as a club to attack and break down the listener's psychological defenses. As the obscenity ages and in turn becomes too popularized, most people build up adequate defenses against it. The obscenity now loses its disruptive potency, tends to become less used, and eventually dies a natural linguistic death by becoming archaic.

This could be considered a new dynamic *psychosocial* theory of the evolution and function of slang and obscenity. It is *psychological* insofar as it deals with the intrapersonal associative structure within an individual; it is *social* insofar as it deals with the dynamics by which emotionally charged impulses are transmitted from one person or group to another. The evolution of slang and the obscene as presented here could have implications for a more general theory of the evolution of new linguistic forms, their functions, transformations, and eventual demise. Language is not a static communication tool, as some would like to believe. Rather, *linguistic invention is a manifestation of the evolution of consciousness and its struggle to perpetually free itself from the limitations and constraints of past usage.*

A gentler use of shock and surprise and the mild use of *hell* is discussed in the next section.[7]

No Such Thing as Hypnotherapy

Hypnotic Approaches to Establish More Adequate Contact: Indirect Shifting of Identity via Use of the Word "Hell"

A minister was asked why his sermons were so successful. He stated: "It is very simple. First I tell my congregation what I am going to tell them, then I tell it to them, and then I tell them what I have told them." This morning I mentioned the clergyman of rather high rank who came to my office. He sat down rather stiffly and rigidly and anxiously, stating that he was there for therapy. I noted his tension and anxiety; I noted the stiffness of his posture. I could speculate on the meaning of these body cues. A clergyman certainly ought to have had enough contact with people to be at ease with them, and yet he was stiff, he was rigid, his voice was clipped and anxious and tense.

Therefore, I really ought to say something. He might be anxious about whether or not I was over-awed by his clerical garb; I really ought to put him at ease. What can you say to a clergyman to make him recognize that he is not a clergyman— he is a patient in your office—and that is why you are interested in him. My statement was very simple: "That is a hell of a mess on my desk, and sometime when I get through straightening out patients, I'll straighten up the desk, too."

Now, you don't say *hell* to a clergyman, but you can say *hell* to a patient, and so using that word classified him immediately as a patient. It is a casual utterance. What does it mean when I said, "When I get through straightening out patients, I'll straighten up the desk, too"? I do straighten out patients, and I can straighten up my desk, too—a nicely indirect but very effective measure of communicating an understanding to the patient. He sighed with relief, relaxed in the chair, and there was no more tension, no more anxiety in his voice. He was no longer concerned about any attitude I had toward his clerical garb; he knew I would treat him as a patient.

This question of hypnotherapy blends itself very, very nicely. *There is really no such thing as hypnotherapy. There is therapy wherein you use hypnotic modalities, hypnotic understanding; but hypnosis in itself is not a therapy.* Hypnosis is a means of establishing a more adequate contact with your patient and a more favorable environment in which your patient can seek to understand the total situation.

Observation: Essence of Diagnostic and Therapeutic Skill

The Case of the Unobserved Double Leg Amputation: Erickson's Hot and Humid Lesson on Observation for His Medical Students

Another point I want to stress is this: For heaven's sake, look at your patient. Really see your patient. I am going to give you an example that involved six unfortunate medical students.

It was a very miserable, hot day in Michigan—so humid and hot. I said to my medical students: "I am delighted to see you gentlemen today. I have one of the easiest cases in the world for you. You do not have to take any history of the patient. *I just want you to look at the patient, and having looked at the patient, to give me a diagnosis.* The patient is 72 years old and is exceedingly psychotic. She will not understand anything you say. She will look at you slightly alert, but she still will not know whether you are dead or alive—she responds in the very same way to inanimate objects as well. She will be lying there in bed, and remember, it is an awfully hot day today. It is terribly humid, and the patient is going to be lying there in bed. You will stand around her bed, three of you on one side and three on the other. You will stand there silently. You will not exchange any ideas. You will not try to question her. You will not look toward each other. Look only at the patient. As soon as you know the diagnosis, come to the nurses' station. I will be back in one hour's time to see if any of you has arrived at the correct diagnosis. I hope you have, because it is going to be difficult to stand here silently for one whole hour on such a wretchedly hot and humid day."

I came back an hour later. I could see the furious looks on the faces of my medical students. They were still standing around the patient's bed, three on each side. Their faces were blank; they were not using their brains at all; they were just using their eyelid motions.

"I see you haven't got the diagnosis yet," I remarked. "Why don't you *look at the patient*. It is an awfully hot, humid day. *Just look at the patient*. As soon as you get the diagnosis, go to the nurses' station and call me. I will be back in an hour's time."

An hour later I returned to the same blank faces. At the end of the third hour I said, "Well, gentlemen, it seems to be a rather hopeless diagnostic case as far as you are all concerned. So let us really *look at the patient*. You know, she has only one scalp and one forehead; she has two eyes and two ears, she has only one nose but two nostrils; she has one mouth and two lips; she has one chin, one neck, two shoulders, two arms—" At this point one of my students sputtered a curious oath. "Go to the nurses' station," I instructed.

Turning back to the other students I continued, "You know, she has two upper arms, two lower arms, two wrists, two hands." Two more students exclaimed, "I'll be damned!", and proceeded to the nurses' station. The three remaining students looked and looked at the patient and finally said, "Okay, okay, this patient is suffering from diabetes mellitus."

Amputation of both upper thighs. A hot, humid day. How much bed clothes were over her? I had draped that sheet very carefully in advance so that they could see exactly where her legs ended. I think patients should be looked at to see if they have two legs! It was obvious that she did not. When you encounter a patient who is 72 years old and has an amputation of both extremities of the upper third of the thighs, you had better start thinking what could lead to that. I wanted my students to think of any disorder that could include the matter of amputation of both legs to the upper third of the thighs. I didn't care if they hit upon diabetes mellitus specifically; all I wanted was any diagnosis that might lead to amputation. But, you know, they had not even noticed the amputation! They had looked only at the patient's face.

Ten years later I got letters from two of my former medical students stating essentially the same idea: "When patients enter my office I count their feet and their arms; I look to see if one eye is made of glass; and I am really enjoying the practice of medicine."

I think it is tremendously important for you to observe everything possible about your patients. Then, if you want to use hypnosis, you know how to verbalize your suggestions to influence your patients, and you know how to listen to their responses. You need to observe patients to get acquainted with them and to recognize the little things they are manifesting.

Keeping Secrets

Utilizing the Negative in a Therapeutic Double Bind to Reveal and Withhold: "Don't Tell Me One Bit More..."

Understand that patients are going to withhold some vital information from you. You will see them laboriously sit down and assume certain positions that you come to recognize as meaning, "I am going to tell you everything except..." You had better believe that they are telling you everything except—. You had better respect (and anticipate) that omission by saying, "I expect you to tell me your entire history. Certainly I don't want you to do it all today. I want you to be

128

willing to withhold certain things until you are really ready to tell me more." In this way I am telling them that they can withhold. This is a hypnotic suggestion which patients cannot possibly recognize. I am saying: "I do not expect you to tell me everything today. I expect you to withhold some of your history until you are willing to tell me *more*." That is right. You create a situation in which patients can move and respond freely, comfortably, safely and securely.

One patient who came to see me made it obvious that she was going to be very restrictive in all of her utterances. I told her: "Now this is your first interview with me, and you are awfully tense; you are awfully anxious. I don't mind that. It is your first visit with a psychiatrist, and you really don't know how to act in the presence of a psychiatrist. Why shouldn't you be anxious? You have some problems which motivated you to come to a psychiatrist, and let us handle this matter carefully. I would like you to tell me your history, but only that part that you are willing to tell me today—and watch yourself carefully. *Don't tell me one bit more than you are really sure you should tell me.*"

The patient relaxed immediately and began telling me her history very comfortably, very easily. She told me about her affairs between the ages of 22 and 27. At the end of the hour she said, "When I came into this office, I was going to watch my tongue. I wasn't going to have a single slip of my tongue. I wasn't going to tell you about my sexual discretions. Now why did I tell you about those affairs?"

"I suppose they are part of your problem," I said, "and that you really want help. You want your thinking clarified, and you want your emotions clarified on the subject of these affairs."

"Yes," she said, "that is right. You see, I want to know just what sort of an adjustment I am going to make to my past history. I am in love with this man, but I have this lurid past history."

"Who defined it as lurid?" I asked.

"I did," she said, "not you. When I told you about my first affair you said to me, 'Are you sure you want to tell me about that yet?' I knew right then and there that I wanted to tell you all about that affair—and about the second one, too. Then you cautioned me again with the question, 'Do you really want to tell me about the second affair?' I knew right then and there that I was going to tell you about the second affair—and about all the others."

You see, I cautioned her. I asked her to hold back.

Rossi: Erickson often told humorous stories about how he would hint to patients that they should keep their "secrets." By simply mentioning the word *secrets,* of course, many emotionally-laden secrets become activated. Perhaps the patient will not reveal his secrets, as in the case Erickson describes here, but a dynamic process is initiated within the patient, nonetheless. It is the activation of such emotionally-laden processes within patients that evokes a sometimes disturbing but often useful tension and unrest that helps them break through their learned limitations and defenses to find their way to cathartic relief and problem-solving.

Indirect Approaches for Establishing Rapport with Young Children

Distraction and Fixation of Attention to Overcome Resistance and Elicit Information: Use of the Negative and "Reluctance to Impose"

How do you treat a small child [who says to you with its behavior], "Please don't come too close to me"? You enter the house and there is this child who needs your attention. The child is sitting over in that remote corner, looking you over with a hostile eye. You walk toward that child and say, "What a pretty little child you are." But the child has its own opinion of your judgment, your tact, and everything else. [I take another approach.] I take my watch off and I look at it and I listen to it and I fiddle around with it; and the child looks and turns the other way. That child isn't going to let me cheat him of looking at my watch.

I tell him: "You *don't* need to come over here to look at my watch. This is my watch." Are you going to give that child orders? Certainly *I* am not. That child is going to let me know a few things, and the first thing the child knows, he is climbing up on my lap and telling me about his bedwetting and the way his mother talks to him, the way his father talks to him. Why shouldn't he? For I haven't forced him into anything. *I have shown a reluctance to impose my personality.* Now as I have said before, adults are only little children grown a little older and a lot taller. They still behave like infants in the medical, dental, or psychological office.

"The Meek Shall Inherit the Dirt"

The Use of Metaphor, Analogy, and
Categorical Statements to Redirect
Attention via Metacommunication

[*There is an inaudible question from the audience.*] I wouldn't dispute the statement that the meek shall inherit the dirt. Somehow or other, in a vague and obscurant way, I would start discussing the joys of making mud pies in childhood. Did you ever eat mud pies when you were a little kid? Wasn't it delightful? It was so confusing when Mother came along and thought your hands were dirty. *Dirty.* Mother really thought they were dirty. How did you feel about it? You had been successful in making mud pies.

What have I done but gone back to childhood? How old were you when you first discovered that there was a kind of creature who made you want to wash your neck and grease your hair? It is important for you to consider this matter of using metaphors, analogies, categorical statements, and so on, to direct your patient's attention from one issue to another. You never avoid what the patient says about dirt!

PART III

Hypnotic Induction And Suggestion

CREATIVE CHOICE IN SENSORY EXPERIENCE AND BEHAVIOR[1]

Learning to Induce Trance

Exercises in Formulating Hypnotic Suggestions: Implied Meanings, Lifetime Understandings, and Time Elements in Suggestion

I think the best way of learning how to induce therapeutic hypnosis is to take pencil and paper and sit down all by yourself and write out 10 or 20 or 30 or 40 or 50 pages of the kinds of suggestions you want to make to a subject. As you write and rewrite these suggestions, you will learn something about your own command of language. You will learn something about your ideas of how to say things to a subject.

You do not tell a subject, "You are getting sleepy." That is a bald statement, and yet how meaningful is it? You really need to set down all your statements, and then analyze them for their actual meaning, and then revise them. It seems like a laborious task, and it really is. But once you have done it—once you have really analyzed all the suggestions you have written down—then you are in a position to understand what suggestions really are. It is much easier after that. You will not need to use the 20, 30, or 40 typewritten pages of suggestions, because you will have some understanding of what it is you have really said.

Many people talk freely and easily and fluently, but if you had a stenographer record their remarks, you would wonder what they did with the periods, the ends of sentences, and that sort of thing. People do not talk in complete sentences; they talk in ideas. In working with hypnotic subjects, you want to communicate an idea. You want to communicate it in a very simple way and in a most effective way. And you want to use the greatest possible economy of words. Furthermore, you want to know exactly what it is you are suggesting to a subject.

"You are getting sleepy" is a bald statement. It is also an emphatic statement, and it seems to carry so much meaning. Remember, that patient has just sat down and is curious about hypnosis. The patient does not really understand very much about the situation. For you to say, "You are getting sleepy" is batting up against a wall of lifetime understandings of sleep as a physiological phenomenon. Immediately you encounter all of the patient's lifetime learnings in connection with the word *sleep*. Everybody lies down on a bed and goes to sleep. Now what does that mean? We do not lie down on the bed *to sleep*; we lie down on the bed *to go to sleep*. There is a time element that everybody naturally expects to occur, and that time element is a very important factor.

Receptivity in Trance Induction

Casual Questions Facilitating a Yes Set; Depotentiating Resistance by Removing It from the Hypnotic Situation; Questions Evoking a No Set

How do you prepare naive subjects for a hypnotic trance? First of all, you want them to be in a receptive frame of mind. *There is nothing more important in inducing a trance than to bring about a receptive frame of mind.* But to ask patients, "Please have a receptive mind," is absurd and ridiculous. How do you get a receptive mind? You merely say a number of things that allow patients to produce that receptive frame of mind by virtue of their own behavior. A patient's behavior is the important focus. The hypnotherapist should adapt himself to whatever behavior the patient manifests.[2]

134

One goes about getting a receptive mind as simply as possible:

"Do you like that chair? Is it comfortable? Would you like to cross your legs? Would you like to drop your hands in your lap? Would you like to have your hands on the arm of the chair?"

In other words, you proceed to ask a number of apparently simple, casual questions, each of which elicits the answer of yes. As soon as you get patients saying yes to this and yes to that—yes, yes, yes, *yes*—you have evoked your receptive frame of mind. You have gotten your patients into the habit of saying *yes*.

When you have resistant patients, you should always see to it that they attach their no's to something that does not enter into the hypnotic situation.

"You do not like smog, do you? No, you do not."

And there is no smog in this room, but you do not specify that there is no smog in this room.

"But you do not like smog. You do not like cold. You do not like traveling over the desert."

All those dislikes are far removed from the immediate hypnotic situation. So you do try to elicit no's from resistant subjects, but you get those no's far away from the hypnotic situation. You get every possible *yes* in the immediate situation. It makes no difference whether the hand is on the arm of the chair or in the lap; whether the person is looking in that direction, or in another direction, or straight ahead.

Directing Motor Behavior

Use of the Word "Perhaps" to Indirectly
Facilitate Sensory-Perceptual Behavior

You can suggest,

"*Perhaps* you would like to look at the picture,"

and patients can speculate upon that suggestion. Then you can suggest that,

"*Perhaps* you would rather look at the candle-sticks."

What have you done? You have directed their gaze here, and you have directed their gaze there. Patients are not aware of the fact that you really have been directing them to do this and to do that. You are taking over the problem of directing their motor behavior.

"Your right arm is on the arm of the chair. Your left arm is in your lap. And *perhaps* you can feel your hand resting on your thigh."

There really is no *perhaps* about it, but "perhaps you can feel it resting on your thigh" is a nice, social way of saying it. But there is no *perhaps* about it. You are not forcing yourself upon them.

"Perhaps you are interested in noticing the texture of the cloth."

What have you done? You have asked the patient to feel her thigh. You have asked her to sense the texture of the cloth. So you are piling up, one after the other, all the varieties of things that she can do and that she is doing. Yet it is only a question of *perhaps*. "*Perhaps* you would like to do this ... *perhaps* you would like to do that." *The important point is that your patient is beginning to obey you and to follow your instructions.*

Free Will: Facilitating Behavior in Children

Obedience and Creative Choice in the Double Bind: Wonder, Interest, and Double Binding Questions to Evoke and Ideomotor Response of Cooperative Behavior

Let us discuss the matter of handling a small child who is not going to pick up his blocks and is ready to fight out that battle to the last ditch. You simply *wonder* if this block should be picked up first, or if that block should be picked up first. What have you really done? *You have sidestepped the issue of picking up blocks by stepping into the problem of picking up blocks.* But it isn't *blocks*; it is *this block* or *that block.*

"And I *wonder* which one should be picked up first?"

But you are only *wondering* about which block should be picked up first, and you are not specifying *who* should pick up which block first. The child cannot think about who should pick up which block first without getting a muscle set, an ideomotor response of, *I'd like to pick up this block first.* That is the response you really wanted in the first place: to have the child pick up the blocks.

Then you say,

"Well, that one over there looks interesting."

What does the child think about? Does the child think about picking it up? Or does the child think about how interesting that block looks as he picks it up? Soon the child is picking up first one block, and then another, and then another. Instead of just picking up blocks, the child is picking up an *interesting* block; and this one before that one, and that one next because it is also interesting; and another one because it is circular, and still another because it is triangular. Thus you move on from one idea to another, to the child's complete satisfaction.

Rossi: In this and the previous section on directing motor behavior, Erickson's position as a transitional figure in the history of hypnosis becomes particularly evident. When he ends the previous section with the sentence, "The important point is that your patient is beginning to obey you and to follow your instructions," Erickson is giving expression to the traditional authoritarian approach of classical hypnosis. However, when he asks the child in this section, "And I *wonder* which one should be picked up first?", Erickson is creating the more permissive mode of the present approaches to hypnotherapy.

Erickson's authoritarian attitude is most apparent in his belief in what Kubie called "illusory choice," as noted previously. This behaviorally compelling aspect of the therapeutic double bind is very evident in Erickson's belief that he is structuring the situation so that the child will obey him in picking up the blocks one way or another. There is also a "*free choice among comparable alternatives*," however, when the child is engaged in deciding *which* of the interesting blocks he will pick up first. What makes this a therapeutic bind is the presence of a "positive metalevel" (a positive presupposition or implication) that motivates and moves the child to the "constructive activity" of picking up the blocks. (The final section of this volume explores the intricacies of various types of double binds in detail.)

This positive metalevel is in the form of a question that has an ideomotor component, "a muscle set," as Erickson calls it. From this example it would appear that the *ideomotor mind-body muscle set* functions as the metalevel structuring the therapeutic double bind. This type of bind that utilizes ideomotor responses was developed extensively in psychosomatic medicine by Erickson's student, David Cheek, M. D.[3]

This type of ideomotor or "mind-body therapeutic bind" has echoes for me in the recent work of Libet when he says, "Voluntary acts can be initiated by unconscious cerebral processes before conscious intention appears."[4] The exciting challenge in all of these associations between Erickson's and Cheek's pioneering work with Libet's current behavioral approach is that it opens up the possibility of new experimental approaches to the "mind-body problem" as well as the basic philosophical issue of free will.[5]

A Fail-Safe Hypnotic Induction

Covering All Possibilities of Response; Implications of "Look Where You Wish to Look"; Training Exercises for the Hypnotherapist

In the matter of inducing a hypnotic trance, you might say: "You probably would like to put your right hand—or is it your left hand—on your lap. And you may leave it there, or you may put it on the arm of the chair. Or you may leave it in your lap and put your left arm on the arm of the chair; or leave it in your lap; or perhaps put it down by your side."

In other words you try to cover every possible phase of activity. No matter what patients do—whether they put their hands down on the chair seat, on their laps, on the arm of the chair, hanging down outside the arm of the chair—it happens to be something that you have mentioned or implied in some way. Therefore, *any behavior on their part is actually in accord with an instruction you have given already.*

You manage to direct your patient's gaze toward that picture and those candlesticks straight ahead.

"But perhaps instead you would rather look at your hand, or perhaps at the floor."

You really don't know what your patient would like to look at.

"Or perhaps you would like to look *where you wish.*"

What does that mean? It means, *I want you to do what you*

wish to do, but it is I *who wants you to do as you wish to do.*

The patient is listening to you but is not analyzing the actual significance of your remarks. So you simply state that, "Perhaps you would like to look *where you wish* to look." The implication is, *You look where you wish because I say so.* The patient is responding, and the more responses you can elicit, the less opportunity the patient has of resisting you in any way.

Now you can see what I mean by writing out suggestions so that you can really understand what your suggestions are communicating. I was very lucky with the first few subjects I hypnotized. Then I began to encounter failure after failure. I thought that was awfully wrong, so I started writing out and trying to understand what I was saying, paragraph by paragraph, sentence by sentence, phrase by phrase. I think I wrote out one technique that came to 50 pages of typewritten material. Then I had a delightful time trying to understand what I had written.

From time to time, I conjure up a hallucinatory subject and try to meet a particular situation that is likely to develop in the office or in an experimental setting.

Utilizing Resistance in Trance Induction

Paradoxical Agreement to Express Resistance;
Attaching Resistance to Nonhypnotic Targets

Just exactly how will you get to a patient who enters your office but is very resistant and uncooperative? The patient is sitting right there in the chair, and you see to it immediately that the patient who is decidedly resistant puts all that resistance right *there* in that chair.

I can remember one patient, a doctor, who walked into the office and plunked himself down in a chair saying, "Hypnotize me, if you can."

My reply was,

"I expect that chair is rather uncomfortable for you
to go to sleep in."

(It really was a comfortable chair, but I supposed that it was not!)

The doctor said, "It certainly is uncomfortable! You ought to get a more comfortable chair for your patients."

I confessed that I really ought to do that, and that I was really at fault.

Next I commented,

"Is that light too bright?",

referring to the floor lamp. Of course, with his resistance it was too bright, so what could he do but agree with me. *But he was agreeing with me in order to express his resistance.* Then I hoped that he did not mind the disorder of the books on my bookcase. He was very forgiving about that, although it was definitely annoying to have books out of line, shoved back and pulled forward and piled on top of one another. *He was agreeing with me and at the same time giving expression to all of those resistances.* I wanted those resistances to be out in the open, and I wanted them attached to the lamp, the bookcase, and the chair.

Then, when it came to the question of putting him in a trance, I discovered that I had to get something out of a filing cabinet. He grudgingly got out of his chair so that I could get at that filing cabinet. It was very simple. There was another chair nearby, and he sat down in that other chair while I fiddled with the filing cabinet. Then I shoved that first chair off to one side. That was the chair that contained all his resistances! So over there in the other chair he could go into a trance. What else could he do? I had very carefully located all his resistances and had him specify them in a positive way. Then I literally moved him out of that chair, leaving behind his resistances.

Anyone who wants to work with patients has to bear in mind that they come to you for the purpose of receiving help. They don't know just how you are going to give it, and neither do you until you see the individual patient. *It is your obligation to give patients that help in the ways they can accept it.* If they want to be exceedingly resistant, why not help them? Give them the opportunity. Certainly in dealing with patients, you have to deal with what they bring into the office. They bring in their resistances; they bring in their receptiveness; their acquiescence. But whatever they bring to you should be something you are willing to use.

Just how will you do it? By writing a hypothetical technique in detail and making it as prolonged and elaborate as can be. You will know what you have written, what your ideas are, and how you can improve upon them.

Formulating Hypnotic Suggestions

Utilizing Continuity, Time, and Sensory Experience;
Analyzing the Phrases,
"As You Sit There" and "Sooner or Later"

Do not suggest, "You go to sleep NOW." What is the person's definition of the word *now*? *Now* means the immediate moment, but *"as you sit there"* is a continuing experience. Furthermore, it is something that the patient is already doing.

"And as you continue to sit there, you will naturally get tired. The human body tends to rest itself by shifting its position. You cross your legs and you uncross them. You alter your position from time to time. Your body tires."

Everybody knows that the body tires. The patient begins to wonder: *When am I going to uncross my legs? When am I going to cross my legs? When am I going to move my hand this way? When am I going to move it that way?*

Patients have a lifetime of somatic experience in the matter of getting tired. You are just reminding them, and by reminding them, you are laying the foundation for them to make responses.

"As you sit there, sooner or later ... " Now who can define those words *sooner* or *later*? We each give our own definition of *sooner* and *later*. For a tortoise that lives 500 years, sooner or later may be this year or ten years from now. For a mayfly that lives only a day or so, sooner or later means within the next few seconds.

> "Sooner or later you may begin to sense a feeling of fatigue in your legs, or your neck, or perhaps your eyes."

Fail-Safe Suggestions

*Permissiveness in Giving Somatic and
Experiential Truisms:
"You May Begin to Sense Fatigue"*

"You may begin to sense . . . " *You may* is one type of statement; to *begin* is another type of word. When do you *begin*? There is no definite time set on the word *begin*. To *sense*: Here again you have made an appeal to the patient. It is *his* sensing, but you have employed three different categories of words: *you may . . . begin . . . to sense*. By using that variety of words, each with a different connotation, very little opportunity remains for the patient to take issue with or controvert or contradict any one of your utterances.

What do you have to dispute? You start at the end of the sentence, *to sense*. Everybody can sense. Then you have to back up to the word *begin*. Everybody begins things, so you cannot dispute that point very well. Then you back up to the word *may*, and that is not a command; it is simply a statement of probability:

> "You *may* begin to sense fatigue."

Fatigue is a reality. Where is the opportunity to dispute or contradict or resist?

Future-Oriented Suggestions

Utilizing Feeling Conducive to Trance: Somatic Processes within the Self: "You Will Undoubtedly Begin to Have Some Feelings"

You try to put things into the future:

"After a while, as you sit there, you probably will get tired of listening to me."

When you are working with patients, it is not a social situation; it is a professional situation.

"You may begin to get tired of listening to me."

That is very true—they probably will—but you want them to! So you transform it from a social situation to a professional situation in that simple way. It is already a professional situation, but you are emphasizing it anew.

"You may begin to get tired."

To get tired: when do you do that? *To get tired* is something that comes out of the future. It is a future possibility, a future contingency. You are always talking in terms of the future, not in terms of the immediate reality.

"And as you get tired of listening to me, you will undoubtedly begin to have some feelings in your body—perhaps in your neck."

You will undoubtedly is a disputable statement, but *begin to have some feelings in your body* makes the disputable statement into one which cannot possibly be disputed. You see, they will have feelings in their bodies. You are utterly certain that your patients will have feelings. So you transfer any disputation from *you will undoubtedly* to an indisputable fact, *you will have feelings in your body.*

144

When you have feelings in your body, what are they? They are feelings of fatigue, feelings that you want to shift the body, feelings that you want to do something. You are directing your patients' attention to ongoing somatic processes *within themselves*. That is where you want the processes. You do not want patients to be reacting to you and to externalities. *You want them to be sensing processes within themselves that are conducive to a hypnotic trance.*

Mother Goose and Lullabies as Fail-Safe Suggestions

Interweaving a Complex Array of Ideodynamic Associations: "Perhaps" Covering All Possibilities of Response, Implication, and Future Orientations

"And as you feel those things more and more clearly, perhaps you will notice a sensation of numbness or fatigue or sleepiness in your foot. Or perhaps you would prefer to have it occur in your hand."

This is similar to what you say to the little child: "Maybe you would like to pick up this block or that block." The question of picking up the blocks has never arisen. Instead it is a question of, "Would you choose *this one* or *that one*?" The *implication* is the effective part.

"Perhaps you will notice a feeling of tiredness or fatigue or pressure in your foot or in your hand."

Everyone of you here in the audience today can sense pressure in your feet, so I am utterly safe in suggesting that to my patients. If your legs are crossed, you can sense pressure in your knees and thighs.

"You will begin to feel that sometime you may want to buy a car" is really a low-pressure sales pitch. The salesman isn't going to get anywhere with that tactic. But then that is dealing with externalities—a car is decidedly external. So far as personal somatic experience is concerned, it is high-pressure salesmanship to say, "You will begin to feel that you are getting sleepy." Your patients are not sleepy yet, that is true. *But* they are beginning to think about that word *sleepy*, which you introduced at a distance—remotely. It is a safe word to introduce because it is in the remote future.

> "And as you begin to feel that you are getting sleepy, you may sense your eyelids blinking. They will blink normally, but you may sense them blinking more rapidly—you may."

No matter what the patient does, whatever you have said is accurate and applicable.

> "You may begin to sense a feeling of sleepiness, and you may notice that while your eyelids blink normally, they may blink more rapidly."

That is not only raising the question, it is raising the interest of the patient in this matter of having the eyelids blink more rapidly.

You tell a patient, "I want your eyelids to blink more rapidly."

The patient says, "And who are you to tell me that!"

You do not want to arouse any resistances of any sort. Your patients come to you to be put into a trance, not to be irritated, not to be ordered around, but to be put asleep. All we need to do is go back to the *Mother Goose* rhymes and the lullabies, and the lulling sound of the ocean waves—a lulling that goes with the idea of sleep. Whether we always recognize it not, we really like to be lulled into inaction. With a hypnotic patient or subject, we make use of that liking for lulling.

Rossi: Erickson's statement, "The implication is the effective part" is of essence for understanding his approach to therapeutic suggestion. The concept of "psychological implication" in hypnotherapy was

146

outlined by Erickson, Rossi, & Rossi (1976) as follows:

"An understanding of how Erickson uses implication will provide us with the clearest model of his indirect approach to hypnotic suggestion. Since his use of "implication" may involve something more than the typical dictionary definition of the term, we will assume that he may be developing a special form of "psychological implication" in his work. For Erickson, psychological implication is a key that automatically turns the tumblers of a patient's associative processes into predictable patterns without awareness of how it happened. The implied thought or response seems to come up autonomously within patients, as if it were their own inner response rather than a suggestion initiated by the therapist. Psychological implication is thus a way of structuring and directing patients' associative processes when they cannot do it for themselves. The therapeutic use of this approach is obvious. If patients have problems because of the limitations of their ability to utilize their own resources, then implications are a way of bypassing these limitations. . . .

"It is important in formulating psychological implications to realize that the therapist only provides a stimulus; the hypnotic aspect of psychological implications is created on an unconscious level by the listener. The most effective aspect of any suggestion is that which stirs the listener's own associations and mental processes that creates hypnotic experience.

"There are, to be sure, crude and mostly ineffective uses of implication in everyday life, where the speaker in a very obvious manner attempts to cast negative implications or aspersions on the listener. In such crude usage the implication is obviously created entirely by the speaker. In our use of psychological implication, however, we mean something quite different. In the psychological climate of the therapeutic encounter the patient is understood to be the center of focus. Every psychological truth is consciously or unconsciously received by the patient for its possible application to himself. Psychological implication thus becomes a valuable indirect approach for evoking and utilizing a patient's own associations to deal with his own problem.

"This was well illustrated when a colleague referred a rebellious teenager to Erickson. He listened quietly to the lad's story and then initiated an important therapeutic development with one simple statement: '*I don't know how your behavior will change.*' The rebellious teenager was in no mood to accept advice from a doctor, and, in truth, Erickson really did not know how his behavior was going to change. By openly admitting that he did not know, Erikson disarmed the lad's resistance so he could momentarily experience an *acceptance set*. Erickson than managed to insert one implication in that moment of the acceptance: 'Your behavior will change.' The boy was now left with the idea of change; his own associations and life experience would have to create exactly how that change was going to take place." (pp. 59-61)

We will return to this concept of *psychological implication* in Part VII of this volume, where we discuss the relationships between unverbalized implications as the basic mechanism for framing paradoxical and double-binding experiences in therapeutic hypnosis and psychotherapy. As we shall see, double-binding psychological implications may also be of essence for understanding the relationships between play, humor, creative breakthroughs, and even "enlightenment" itself in the practice of Zen.

Transforming Future Orientations
into Immediate Reality

*Accommodating the Need for Trance Without Awareness:
The Use of "Or" to Cover All Possibilities of Response*

"While you are getting sleepy, you may begin to
feel that you are getting sleepy."

While you are getting sleepy has transformed that original,
future-oriented suggestion into an immediate reality of *while
you are getting sleepy*. The words *while you are getting sleepy*
imply that the sleepiness is taking place right now, and there
is no way of disputing it, no way of taking issue with it.

"While you are getting sleepy, perhaps you would
like to shift your right hand from the arm of the
chair to your lap. Or perhaps you would like to let
it remain on the arm of the chair."

What have you actually suggested to your patients? You
have suggested that *they are getting sleepy*, because while
they are getting sleepy, they are going to do one of two things.
They are either going to put their hands in their laps or on the
arm of the chair *while they are going to sleep*! So you have
gotten across that suggestion of going to sleep.

"And later as you begin to feel yourself going
deeper asleep, you may want to move your left
hand, or you may want to let it remain still."

Either you move your left hand or you let it remain still—
either way, the hypnotist has given a suggestion, and no matter
what patients do, they are obeying that suggestion. You are
giving a wealth of suggestions constantly but without letting
your patients know. They do not really want to know; what
they want is to be put into a trance. Patients have the idea that
they should go into a trance—pass out—and not know what is

going on around them. Why not accommodate them as far as possible? Do not let them know what the suggestions are that you are giving. Just present them with the suggestions in such a way that they can accept them.

Play as Therapeutic Binds with Children

Evoking Curiosity, Wonder, and Behavior via
Double-Binding Questions: Allan's Bedtime Ritual:
"I'm Not Going to Bed!"

One of my sons, Allan, objected very strenuously to undressing and going to bed at night. It was really marvelous sport! We did not want to undress him; we did not want to force him to undress; we did not want to force him to go to bed. So I always wondered if he would like to put one shoe under this table and the other shoe under that table, and his shirt over there, and his pants over there. It really was fun. Then all of a sudden, when he found himself in the nude, there would be that look on his face of *now what have I done*! It was really delightful to watch his expressive face. What had happened? It was so delightful to hide a shoe here and hide a shoe there, and a shirt there—and now he is in the nude! How did that happen?

Sometimes I would take great pleasure in anticipating him and wondering whether he was going to have two pillows or one pillow; whether he was going to lie on the front side of the bed or the back side of the bed; whether he was going to have a sheet over him, or a sheet and a blanket. We would really investigate all those matters. Then when he said good night— "Now where am I?!", he would sigh, "Oh, well," and roll over and go to sleep. What else could he do? He never did have a chance to resist. He really enjoyed it, and night after night he would come to me and say, "I'm not going to go to bed!" I would say, "Well, why should you? But I wonder if Mother can find your shoe if you hide it there."

Why did he come to me and announce, "I'm not going to go to bed?" It was really a delightful game that he enjoyed just as much as I enjoyed it.

Utilizing Spontaneous Behavior

Utilizing the Comparative and Implication to
Deepen Trance and Evoke
"Perfectly Remarkable Things"

Your hypnotic subjects can play that same sort of game with you. Each hypnotic subject is a human personality who likes to be played up to. Your patients have come to you for a very definite purpose. Perhaps they have come because of a specific phobia. How often do you need to mention that phobia? They have come to you for that reason; they have told you about the phobia. You do not need to mention it ever again. As long as those patients are in your office, and you are in your office, and you are both working together, the actuality of that phobia is foremost in your minds. All of you know about it.

When you go for a drive in a car, you never need to assure the driver that he is in the car; and the driver never needs to assure you that you are in the car. You both know it. You are both there, and there is no need to verbalize the fact that you are both in the car. With patients who want to go into a trance, there is no reason why you should keep telling them, "I'm going to put you in a trance; I hope to put you in a trance." That purpose is already paramount in their mind; it is paramount in your mind; it does not need any repetition. Your mere existence confirms it, and neither one of you is going to forget it. By just assuming it as an actuality—as, indeed, it is—you make it easier for patients, because there is no need to keep reminding everybody about the situation.

Consider the words:

"Now as you begin to get more and more sleepy—".

As you begin [pause] to get more and more sleepy: First you must have the positive *to sleep* before you can get the comparative of *sleepier*! That is assumed in the statement. If patients accept the idea of getting sleepier, then they are unconsciously, unwittingly, unknowingly admitting that sleepiness has already begun.

> "And as you get more and more sleepy, you may notice certain things about your body. You might even forget the feelings in your feet or your hands. You may even do that."

It is pretty hard to forget the feelings of your own body, but when you say, "You might even forget," you are actually communicating the idea,

> "You may even do perfectly remarkable things."

You keep introducing ideas very gently, very gradually.

I am being laborious and detailed about this point because I think that everyone of you should write out 20, 30, 40, 50 pages of suggestions that you would give. And you ought to imagine a subject who is resistant, a subject who is cooperative, and write out all the suggestions that you would give.

How would you get a patient to lift his arm from the arm of a chair to his lap? You can do it by asking him; you can do it by telling him. But how else can you do it? Can you direct his attention to the wall? Can you bring about a change in his position so that he just naturally shifts from the arm of the chair to his lap without knowing that he has done so? You want to evoke all the spontaneous behavior within your patient that fits in with your purposes and with his or her purposes.

Indirectness in Psychotherapy

Utilizing Indirect Questions, Oblique Verbal Cues, and Rhythm

To try to get things to happen directly is one way. In psychotherapy, it is always better to get things happening indirectly.

152

"Tell me why you hate the color black"!

Where are you with that question? Behind the eight ball, thoroughly, and so is your patient. How could you introduce the subject of the color black? There are many, many ways of introducing the subject of the color black. You try to do it *indirectly*:

> "There is the blueness of the sky, and you've got darkness around you. There is the blueness of the sky and the brightness of the stars, and you've got darkness around you."

Your patient thinks you are talking about the stars and the blue sky, but you really are talking about the darkness.

> "As you enter the house, you turn on the light."

Again you have introduced the idea of darkness and blackness, which you need a light to dispel. You have established the connotation of darkness, and what is darkness but blackness? Anyway that you can bring about the ideas indirectly is better, because anybody can guard against something that is named. In psychotherapy, you do not want your patients guarding against things. You want them to feel free to give expression to ideas; you want them to express ideas freely and comfortably.

A patient tells you, "There is something wrong with me. I don't know what it is, and I don't want to find out because I am terribly afraid. Won't you be careful not to say anything that makes me afraid?"

I tell the patient:

> "I would be delighted to discuss every innocent thing possible with you and not to mention anything that makes you afraid. Suppose you tell me the things to talk about, and I'll try to avoid those topics that frighten you."

That sounds very reassuring and the patient responds: "I

like painting, I like art, and I like music—especially at night."

Especially at night: now why was that phrase thrown in? "I like painting, I like art, and I like music—*especially at night*." The patient has no guard against those three words. But I can hear them, and I wonder about that music and painting and art. There is rhythm in music, isn't there? And rhythm has a multitude of connotations. I wonder what kind of rhythmic music the patient likes. A rapid rhythm? A slow rhythm? The patient tells me, "I like slow, rhythmic music, but why am I beginning to perspire?" I tell him the room is probably warm, or perhaps he is tense because he has come into the office to discuss a problem. That is an honest answer. I have given an explanation of why he is perspiring. So far I have gotten perspiration, rhythm, and the words, *especially at night.*

Utilizing Implication and Multiple Levels of Meaning

Permissive, Double-Binding
Questions for Eye Closure
("Hobson's Choice")

What kind of painting does the patient like? Pastel colors? No—heavy, dark colors. The mountains at night—again there is that word *night*. So far as the patient knows, I have heard only the word *mountains*, but actually I listened to the word *night*.

"What are the things you think of then?"

The patient thinks I am asking, "What are the things you think of *then*, when you are enjoying the mountains at night? What are the things you think of *then*?" Let the patient put the meaning upon the word *then*. The questions of perspiration, rhythm, and "*especially at night*" have all been mentioned, and then you ask, "What do you think about *then*?" The emphasis upon the word *then* is the tremendously important thing.

So the patient tells me what he thinks about then. As a child he liked the mountains, or he liked the water, or he liked this and that—*as a child*. And as a child, I liked Sorghum on bread. But what does as say about what I like now? It actually tells you that I don't like Sorghum now. That is the implication. One always deals with those implications—with the implied meanings. Yet whenever your patients want to present resistance, you are still in a safe position.

"What did you think about *then*?" You can apply that word *then* to the pictures of the mountains, but *then* also applies to that perspiration—*especially at night*, and so on. I seem to be digressing, but I want to illustrate this matter of making use of words in inductions that carry a wealth of meaning.

"As you begin to get more and more sleepy, you may notice a numbness or pressure in your legs, in your hands; and your eyes may blink shut. *For a moment or two*, your eyes may blink *shut*."

For a moment or two—but I have said the word *shut*. Then I qualified it with the phrase, "for a moment or two." How do patients deal with that communication? They have to deal with *shut, in a moment*, and *or two*. How long is a moment or two? It is an indefinite period of time. The spacing of my words actually gives it an indefinite period of time.

"But perhaps instead of shutting your eyes, you want them only a quarter shut."

But perhaps instead of shutting your eyes, you want them only a quarter shut. What is the choice? It is either *shut your eyes*, or have them a *quarter shut*! And there is no escape from that bind.

"Shall we pick up this block or that block?"

Always you present that sort of Hobson's Choice.

"Manipulation" and Choice in Psychotherapy

*Erickson's Ethical Reframing of Manipulation as
"zArousing a Wealth of Ideas"*

These approaches are fair to patients. I have been criti-
cized for manipulating my patients. But why do they come to
see me except to have me *do* something? You do not go to the
dentist to have him pass the time of day with you. You may not
want to have him shoving two thousand instruments in your
mouth and then asking you how many children you have, but
that is what you go to the dentist for: to have a lot of
instruments shoved into your mouth. You expect it. Similarly,
the hypnotic subject should have in his unconscious mind the
realization that *you are manipulating him: You really are
arousing a wealth of ideas in him.*

> "As you begin to get more and more sleepy, you
> may wonder about how soundly asleep you can
> go. And I would like to have you go as soundly
> asleep as you wish and as you can go."

As you wish and *as you can go*: What are the limits you are
suggesting to the subject with these phrases?

> "I would like to have you go to sleep as deeply as
> *you* wish."

Somehow or other that first pronoun *I* has dropped out and
been replaced by the second pronoun *you*—as deeply as *you*
wish. It is a suggestion and a challenge.

> "And you can probably go as deeply asleep as you
> really want to go—*as you really want to go.*"

Rossi: Here again we encounter the curious paradox of
Erickson enhancing the patient's "wealth of ideas"
and the possibilities of creative choice even while he

156

is using manipulation. Certainly Erickson is not "manipulating" in the colloquial sense of controlling and limiting someone for personal advantage. This is the reason I prefer to use words like *facilitating* or *evoking* rather than *manipulating* when discussing the spirit and essence of Erickson's attitude.

PART IV

Choice, Paradox, And Meaning In Hypnotherapy[1]

Alleviating Pain and Resistance in an Orthopedic Injury

A Creative, Challenging Bind to "Describe All of the Feelings You Would like to Have" : Reframing the "Black Art of Hypnosis"

I am supposed to talk on the subjects of anxiety and resistance. Rather than giving a general dissertation on these subjects, I think I'd better illustrate my points by citing cases that present actual problems.

I can think of one patient in particular whose case is exceedingly informative. This patient had been hospitalized from September until I saw her in February. Her physicians had decided to give up on her. She had been receiving narcotics every four hours—excessive doses—a quarter grain of morphine and 100mg. of Demerol, sometimes potentiated with a dose of Percodan. Thirteen years previously she had fallen down stairs. She had undergone a couple of operations, but she still had pain, and it was genuine pain. The orthopedic surgeons were afraid to operate on her because they didn't think that they would be successful.

She was brought by ambulance in a wheel chair into my office, which is in my home. She came in holding her hand in this way. I don't know how many of you realize that his position is an indication of spinal pain. Her doctor called it a "hot thumb," but there was no question in anyone's mind that she was suffering very severe pain. As I listened to her, as I talked to her, I became very, very sure that she was in continuous, acute pain. She was also blazing with resentment, because she thought hypnosis was a black art—*magic*—and she did *not* want to be hypnotized. She thought it was ridiculous, that it was an insult, that it was an indignity. She told me so, very frankly and very angrily, that she did *not* want to be hypnotized; she did *not* want to be subjected to that sort of black art. She stated that the doctors ought to operate on her; they ought to do something reasonable, something sensible, something within the area of medicine.

She wanted to know if I thought her pain was purely imaginary, because if I thought it was purely imaginary, then I ought to have my head examined! It was really pain! Here was a resentful patient. She was anxious to be treated, but she was fearful of the future; she couldn't see any future without an operation, yet she dreaded another operation. She was concerned about the fact that her hospital insurance was running out, and that she would have to live with her sister, whom she hated. There simply was nothing left in her world except misery and pain and distress.

What ought you to do in the way of using hypnotic techniques with such a patient? I let her explain her resentment, her hostility, her anxiety, her distress; and then I asked her simply to describe that pain. As she described the pain, she told me that it was acute. She had long experience with the sensation of pain. I kept asking her to give me the course of the pain: where she felt it and how she felt it. What were the attributes of that pain? What were the particular qualities of the pain? Why did she think hypnosis was a black art? Why did she think her doctor sent her to me? Why did she think she ought to depend upon drugs? What did she think about taking drugs every four hours, six times a day, from September to February? What kind of a drug addict was she?

She resented my calling her a drug addict, and that only intensified her anger and her resistance and her antagonism, and made the situation worse! My statement to her was the following:

> "You are going to stay in this office until the ambulance comes and then the attendants will wheel you out of here. Meanwhile, I am going to talk to you, and you are here to get whatever benefit you can get. I think you are reasonably intelligent, and if you exercise your intelligence, you really ought to find some way of getting some kind of benefit. I really don't care what kind of benefit you receive, so long as you take the benefit that is available to you."

Now, that was putting the burden upon *her:* she had to take the benefit that she could get, the benefit that she could derive from the situation. I challenged her intelligence. Then I stated to her:

> "The fact that you call hypnosis a black art is plain childishness, plain idiocy! And yet, in the back of your mind, you do know that the hospital sent you over here. You do know that all of the physicians who have seen you have suggested that you ought to see me; that I could help you. Some of them were emphatic. Many of them objected seriously to the amount of medication that you are getting. I don't believe you like it either. Therefore, there must be something more than black art, childishness, and mysteriousness to this business of hypnosis, and it is up to your intelligence to select the values that I present to you.
>
> "Now, describe your pain still more. I notice that your thumb really hurts—you are holding it in the right way. I know from personal experience that pain can manifest itself in that particular way. Therefore, describe your pain for me, and describe the particular kind of feeling that you would like to have generalized. Describe the localized feelings

that you would like to feel. *You are going to be able to describe in detail all of the feelings you would like to have."*

This was a challenge to her. When I told her that she would be able to describe the relief, the comfort, the kind of feeling she would like to have, *I was literally putting her in a bind to describe them!* And as surely as she started to describe them, she would want to *sense* them. How better can you describe a thing than by sensing it first? How well can you describe a visual scene except by closing your eyes, and visualizing it, and looking at the various parts of your visualization? She literally had to *sense* the various feelings of comfort that she wanted to have in order to talk about the various kinds of comfort she would like to have.

Indirect Trance Induction

Utilizing Questions and Self-Report to Focus Attention within; Wondering about the Feelings of Warmth and Comfort; Learning the Rituals of Authoritative and Permissive Hypnotic Technique

She would like to have her hand less tense . . . and I watched her hand sowly open . . . and she would like to be able to put her hand on her lap, with her palm resting comfortably on her thigh, instead of tending to hold it up. I kept her talking and describing, always asking little questions as if I didn't fully understand. Now, I can't really tell you what those questions were, because I had to watch my patient, I had to see what she was doing, and I had to fit my questions to each one of her movements. I pointed out to her that she could think better if she closed her eyes, because it would help her exclude her view of me; it would exclude her view of the filing cabinet, and she could attend solely to the processes within herself. *She didn't recognize that when I told her to attend to the processes within herself, she was being asked literally to go into a hypnotic trance.* As she attended to the processes within

162

herself, she would withdraw her attention from external reality, she would limit her degree of consciousness and her feeling of conscious awareness.[2]

I made no recognizable attempt to induce hypnosis, and this is what I want to emphasize to all of you. This matter of using a formal, ritualistic induction of a trance state ("Now fixate on a spot; look at the spot on the wall") really isn't pertinent to the patient's condition or to the goals of increasing relaxation that you want to achieve. *What you want the patient to do is to make the responses that are pertinent to the condition itself, and not for a state of hypnosis.* But I do think you ought to learn every one of the traditional techniques of inducing hypnosis; every one of the rituals of verbal suggestion, every possible indirect or direct authoritative or permissive technique. Learn it very, very well, so that no matter what the situation is, you can have any part of any technique at the tip of your tongue.

That is exactly what I did with this patient. I asked her to put her hand, palm down, on her thigh. Yet, *my request was in response to things that had started within her.* I asked her to continue to describe the sense of comfort she would get, and I wondered if she could actually sense the feeling of warmth from her thigh to her palm, from her palm to her thigh. I just wondered if she could. I wasn't *telling her* to do it. *I was just wondering if she could.* Since she had withdrawn her attention from external reality and was attending to processes within herself, she began sensing the warmth and the comfort in her left hand.

Facilitating Hypnotic Dissociation and Comfort

Extending Feelings of Comfort via Comparison; Utilizing Resistance and Resentment: "Just Bear with Me"

Then I asked her if she could compare her left hand with the right hand that didn't show that clinching of the fingers around the right thumb. She began curiously to explore. What

I was doing was extending the feeling of inner awareness from the left hand to the right hand and making it all-embracing. I pointed out to her that it really wasn't necessary for her to sense the feeling of her feet on the footrest of the wheel chair, because that was unnecessary, and I hoped she would bear with me when I mentioned unnecessary things. I asked her to bear with me. In other words, I was telling her, literally, to go on and resent me, resent my unnecessary remarks. I was recognizing that she was having to put up with a very undesirable person. But when I told her to put up with an undesirable person, I was giving her a suggestion [by utilizing her resistance against me]. She couldn't possibly understand it in that fashion, since I just hoped she would bear with me when I did unnecessary things.

As I pointed out to her, she *did not* need to give her attention to sensations in her feet. I was literally dissociating her feet, dissociating her legs, dissociating her by starting with dissociation in her feet without her awareness. I told her that she could do all of her thinking within her own mind as she listened to my voice. When I said, "my voice," what was I doing? I was removing myself as a hated person, as a resented person, as a person to whom she directed attention or antagonism. As she listened to my voice, I reduced myself to just a voice; and I suggested that as she listened to my voice, she could do more and more things in studying the sensations of comfort that she wanted.

Within 20 minutes the patient was in a very satisfactory trance state. My secretary knocked on the door and called to me about a long-distance phone call, but the patient did not hear me tell the secretary to come in and bring the phone. She was too busy attending to the feelings within herself. So I took my telephone call and dismissed my secretary. She closed the door as she walked out, but my patient was still exceedingly busy not noticing us. I resumed speaking from where I had left off in my remarks to her, so that she did not appreciate the fact that there had been an interruption.

Rossi: Erickson's casual mention of the fact that "within 20 minutes the patient was in a very satisfactory trance state" is consistent with current research indicating there may be natural circadian (once every 24 hours) and ultradian (more than once a day) rhythms of hypnotic responsivity.[3] When patients are asked to "*go into a therapeutic hypnotic trance and take as long as you need to resolve that problem,*" they will typically remain in trance between 15 and 20 minutes.[4] The ultimate significance of this ultradian-circadian theory is that *hypnotic suggestion may be conceptualized as a psychobiological process of "entraining" or "synchronizing" our natural rhythms of rest, rejuvenation, and healing.*

We all experience a natural ultradian Basic Rest-Activity Cycle (BRAC) every 90 to 120 minutes throughout the day and night. At night we tend to dream for 20 to 30 minutes every 90 to 125 minutes or so. Most people feel a need to take a 20-minute "break" every 90 to 120 minutes throughout the day. I have presented evidence that supports the view that these 20-minute rest periods correspond to what Erickson called the "common everyday trance" and what earlier workers such as Charcot called the "hypnoidal states" and Janet called the "*abaissement du niveau mental.*"[5] These earlier workers (as well as Freud and Jung) surmised that there was a relationship between these hypnoidal states, stress, psychopathology, and creativity, but they did not know what it was.

I hypothesize that they were all recognizing many of the behavioral manifestations of ultradian states without knowing that these were natural psychobiological rhythms. Since it is now known that many basic biological processes such as cell division and hormonal activity (particularly the stress, sexual, and growth hormones) all have ultradian rhythms, I have conjectured that many stress problems are due to our unwilling overriding of our natural rhythms to the point of pathological desynchronization. Many therapeutic effects of hypnotic suggestion, on the other hand, may involve the resynchronization and the therapeutic "entrainment" of these natural biological rhythms.

It is well known that ultradian rhythms are easily modulated by many psychosocial stimuli as well as by environmental cues that are called "*zeitgebers*" (time givers, such as daylight cuing us to awaken). According to this view, therapeutic suggestion is simply of a class of psychosocial stimuli that can facilitate our natural psychobiological rhythms of healing. The fact that the conversion of short- to long-term memory has recently been shown to involve similar 90-120-minute ultradian rhythms[6] strengthens the idea the the hypnotic entrainment of many rhythmic psychobiological processes brings us a step closer to understanding what Erickson calls the "psycho-neuro-physiological" basis of hypnosis. In short, the natural psychobiological variation we experience in our ultradian-circadian rhythms is the "basic stuff" of hypnotherapeutic suggestion.

Trance Deepening

Facilitating Time Distortion and Somnambulistic Trance;
"Plain Speaking" to Communicate Fearlessness

You begin a sentence with a patient. You interrupt the sentence, and then you continue, and then you interrupt it, and then you continue it. What are you doing? You are making the patient appreciate the lapse of time. You are making him await your resumption of what you are going to say. But he is going to be waiting for what you say, so when my secretary interrupted me with the phone call, I left off in the middle of a sentence—remembering the last word—took my phone call, dismissed my secretary, and then went on with the next logical word and completed my sentence. I wanted time distortion to develop within the patient so that time would seem, literally, endless or very brief, or in whatever other way she wanted time to be experienced.

And as she continued going deeper and deeper into a somnambulistic trance, my suggestion was that the tensions that derived from pain were unnecessary for her continued existence. Every patient who has serious pain is a patient who is going to wonder about his or her continued existence. If you are ever afraid to say a word or to name a condition to a patient, you are going to alert the patient to the fact that you are afraid. That is why, when I deal with a cancer patient, I say the word *cancer*. I can say very freely,

> "It is the pain in your belly that is going to kill you. You know it and I know it. For as long as you live, and you want to live as long as you can, you want to be free of that pain."

The patient hears me say those unlovely words of *pain* and *kill* and *cancer*—but they are said fearlessly, casually, in an explanatory fashion, presenting an idea.

Paradoxical Therapy with Resistant Patients

Prescribing the Symptom: Depotentiating Resistance by Offering Suggestions the Patient Will Reject; the Indirect Way of Reverse Suggestion; Using Intonation, Inflection, and Pauses

So I spoke to this patient about her tensions.

> "Now what tensions do you really need? I think the tension is something that intensifies pain. I think that you can feel pain much more easily if you tense up, and the more you tense up, the more acutely you can feel pain."

What she did not realize was that I was asking her to tense up and to feel her pain more acutely, and as she felt her pain more acutely, she could recognize that she simply did not want to tense up. So she could take out her antagonism and her

167

resistance toward me by rejecting my suggestions that she tense up. Why shouldn't I give her something to reject?

Whenever you have a patient who is rejecting, who is antagonistic, who is resistant, you ought to appreciate the fact that they are resistant patients, that they are antagonistic; and you ought to be able to mention *antagonism* and *resentment* in such a fashion that they can take the initiative in rejecting that antagonism, in rejecting that resistance, and in achieving the relaxation that you want them to achieve. It is the indirect, the roundabout way. When you tell patients who are antagonistic or resentful to relax, their feeling is, *"Why should I relax?"* But when you suggest that they tense up as you are explaining how pain is intensified, that is another matter entirely. Bear in mind what you have said: "Tense up."

This point emphasizes the importance of intonation, the use of inflections, and the use of pauses to convey your ideas. I suggested to this patient in an explanatory fashion that she would feel the pain much more acutely if she tensed up ("The more you tense up, the more you feel the pain . . . "), instead of saying, " . . . the more comfortable you will be, the more you relax." I did it in the reverse fashion *by offering suggestions that she could reject.*

For the remainder of the hour I continued offering suggestions about her pain that were really suggestions for the rejection of her pain—without telling her to reject the pain. I simply explained the situation repetitiously in a boresome fashion, so that she would get rather tired of listening to what I had to say, so that she would withdraw more and more within herself. At the end of the hour I told her that she would feel very relieved when she got out of the office away from me; that *it would be a relief to be going back to the hospital bed,* and that she would enjoy continuously the thought of being away from me. Yes, she would be away from me. It might be a week before she saw me again, and *it would be such a relief to be out of my presence for another whole long week—such a relief for a whole long week.* She never did have an opportunity to analyze all the suggestions that I was offering her.

Metalevels of Meaning

*Interspersing Indirect Therapeutic Suggestions While
Utilizing Resistance; The Important Role of Nurses*

When you want to deal with patients, I think all of you
ought to write out your speculative theoretical suggestions,
and you ought to analyze them for the content and the meaning
of the individual words; content and meaning of the individual
phrases; content and meaning of the individual sentences.
You ought to recognize how you put into a word or a phrase
or a clause or a sentence a meaning that is quite opposite to its
apparent, overt meaning.

"And it would be a relief to be away from me for a
long, long week of comfort in the hospital."

I accepted readily, freely, comfortably, all of my patient's
antagonism toward me. When she was returned to the hospital, I phoned her physician who told me that he would be
dropping in to see her within the hour. His statement after
seeing her was: "I don't know what you did to that woman, but
this is the first time that I have seen her when she didn't snarl
at me, when she didn't demand that I give her an increased
amount of drugs."

Furthermore, the patient did not ask the nurse for drugs;
she rested comfortably the rest of the day; she went to sleep
that night and didn't wake up during the night to ask for any
medication.

In accordance with my suggestion, the next morning the
nurse came in and stated:

"The doctor said I have to give you this injection
this morning."

I have to give you this injection this morning. What does that
mean? It means that the nurse had to do something that she felt
was unnecessary, and that she would have to do it this

morning, even though it were unnecessary. That evening the nurse said:

> "I have to give you this injection before you go to sleep,"

and she did have to give the injection before the patient went to sleep. But the patient was reduced from six doses of medication (1/4 grain of morphine, 100mg. of demerol, and Percodan) to one dose in the morning and one in the evening.

The nurses also were given the exact words they were to use when they brought in the tray:

> "I am sorry I could not bring you more of this particular item of food."

What does that mean? It means that the quantity of chicken, for example, is insufficient, and that the patient could feel deprived so far as her portion of chicken was concerned. So the patient ate more, and she ate with a better appetite.

You can *ask* a patient to have a better appetite. You can ask a patient to enjoy food increasingly well, but you can also have the nurse apologize because she cannot bring more food.

> "I will be able to bring you *at least half a glass of milk,* in addition to this glassful."

This careful phrasing made it possible for the nurse to bring *two* glasses of milk, because she had said: " . . . *at least half a glass of milk, in addition to this glassful.*" In other words, the nurse was limited but the patient was not limited. Everything the nurses said to that particular patient had been written out ahead of time, and the nurses were coached by the physician so that they would say the right things.

> "I am sorry I won't be able to fix your bed before such-and-such an hour"

means

"I want you to be uncomfortable at that hour because your bed isn't fixed."

So the patient reserves discomfort for ten o'clock. Then the nurse comes in at 9:30 because she has managed to get away. But the patient has been reserving her discomfort for ten o'clock, so when the nurse arrives ahead of time, the patient doesn't need to have any discomfort!

Provoking Pain Relief

Utilizing Partial Symptom Prescription to Evoke Partial Symptom Relief; Directing Pain to the Thumb; Creating a Scapegoat for Failure

I saw this patient twice over a period of two weeks time, and she was free of pain except for that morning dosage and that evening dosage. I had told her that none of us is perfect:

"Certainly you aren't perfect; therefore, you cannot expect complete relief from pain."

What was I really telling her? I was telling her that none of us is perfect—an acceptable statement. None of us is perfect, and "certainly you aren't perfect" (which was an insulting remark), and "therefore, you are going to feel some pain." In her resentment toward me, in her resentment toward that insulting remark, she made up her mind that she would see to it that she felt very little pain.

Why shouldn't I say it that way? It put her on her mettle to see to it that she was much more perfect than I thought her to be. Therefore, there was the opportunity for her to experience some pain, because I knew, as any medical man should know, that you cannot completely abolish pain of an organic origin, but you can ask your patient to reduce the awareness of it. But when you ask patients directly to reduce their awareness of pain, you are asking them to do something to which they can reply with a question: "How is that possible?" You need to put

171

it to them in such a way that the question of the possibility or the impossibility of it does not arise; that they have the opportunity of taking the attitude that there will be pain, but it won't be very much, and that there is a large possibility of becoming unaware of the pain. And whenever pain does occur, they can take the attitude: *This is an inconsequential pain.*

I also apologized to this patient for *all of the pain that was in her thumb.* Now, all of her pain included all of her back, too; it included all of her arms; it included all of her neck. When I said, "all of the pain in your thumb," I was literally directing all of her pain to her thumb. She didn't know that, but I knew what I was saying and why I was saying it. All the pain in her thumb really could not be abolished, and I was sorry that I would fail her. What does that mean? *I was sorry I would fail* means that *I* will fail but that *you* will succeed. I am avoiding the pronoun *you;* I am emphasizing the personal pronoun, *I.* She is going to emphasize her personal estimation of me, and the failure is mine and the success is *hers.* I am literally taking all of the failure upon myself and giving her all of the success. Why shouldn't I do that? She has to have some kind of a scapegoat; she has to have some way of attributing failure to something, to somebody. Why shouldn't I define that particular person?

A week after that first interview, she asked the nurses rather angrily: "Why do I have to go to see that doctor again?" Now, that was a very nice question. Why did she? What does that question imply? She also said: "Why shouldn't I be able to go home to my sister's?" Now, she had disliked her sister for many years. Why shouldn't she dislike me instead of her sister? "Why shouldn't I go to my sister's?" She was being deprived of her right by being sent to me instead of to her sister's. She came to see me and I told her:

"I expect this visit of yours to me to be just as unpleasant for you as you hope it is for me."

What is the correct answer to that? The correct answer to that is: "It is not unpleasant for me, but I will see to it that it is unpleasant for you." That is the correct reaction. Well, I knew that. I know what human responses are, and I could see that nice, sarcastic smile on her face. She wasn't going to tell me that it would be unpleasant *only for me*. She was going to see to it that it was unpleasant for me but not for her. She went into trance and I went through the same particular procedure I had used in our first session. A week later she was dismissed from the hospital at her request. She said she didn't need any further hospitalization, and she went to her sister's, and she is still there.

The orthopedic surgeons are wondering what is going to happen. They do not want to operate. They do not think it will serve any particular purpose, because she has had too many operations. They see no way of relieving her pain, but they do have the feeling that she is going to get along much more satisfactorily. I had carefully pointed out to her:

"Everybody can be weak enough to rely upon medication."

What had I done there? I had given her the opportunity of showing me her strength. And everybody can be so weak and rely upon medication week after week and month after month. But she is still showing me her strength. Why shouldn't she?

Interspersal Technique

Treating Obesity Plus Sciatic Pain via Therapeutic Metalevels; Learning Pain Relief Indirectly and via Time Distortion; Putting "Headlines" on Your Face and in Your Voice; Phrasing and Intonation of Suggestion to Facilitate Unconscious Processes

For my next topic, I thought I would discuss a patient with a different type of problem. Let us call her Mrs. Jones. Mrs. Jones is five feet tall. At the time I saw her she weighed 255 pounds. She had been in the hospital for two months on an 800-calorie diet but had not lost any weight. She was the object of much study because of her failure to lose weight on 800 calories. There was no cheating; there was no smuggling of food of any sort. She was very conscientious; you couldn't possibly get her to cheat, and yet on 800 calories a day, she maintained her weight of 255 pounds.

She has two discs out of place, which create a great deal of pain—continuous sciatic pain. The hospital sent her to see me in the ambulance. I noticed the way she sat in her wheel chair, and she does have sciatic pain. You can only sit in a chair in a certain way if you have genuine sciatica, and she has it. She is a very sweet personality; she is a very honest personality. I liked her immediately, and I was immensely impressed by the tremendous amount of anxiety she had—anxiety that surrounded her like smog surrounds Los Angeles. It was impenetrable.

She was very anxious in her statement that she hoped I could do something for her, but it was obvious that she didn't really expect anything to be done for her. The orthopedic surgeons who had examined her repeatedly had refused to accept her as a patient because they felt that she was too much of a risk with her weight. Then, in addition to her weight, she was having between one and five major epileptic seizures a day; and they really didn't want to operate on her. She was limited to a quarter grain of morphine, and 100mg. of Demerol every four hours, night and day. She didn't take Percodan.

She told me very simply and very earnestly that the drugs helped for about one hour, and that she did appreciate that one hour of relief from pain. She was very much concerned about the fact that she had such a tremendous longing to get another shot; she was convinced she was a drug addict, and what could she do? She didn't want to be a drug addict. Yet all she could think of would be: *When do I get my next shot?* She couldn't read or converse with people because of the fact that her mind was on the time of the next shot. The only time she could really converse was when she had just received a shot, and during the next hour while she felt free of pain. She added that she was concerned about the fact that her doctors had withheld the dosage, and she was there to see me at the beginning of the next period without a shot—she was entering into a four-hour period of pain.

As I looked at the twitching in her face and the quivering of her body, I knew that the woman was obviously in pain. The way in which she spoke expressed pain. I asked her what she thought I could do her? She said: "All of the doctors have tried very, very hard and couldn't succeed." Powerful drugs couldn't succeed, and she honestly did not know how words could help her. I asked her what words she thought might help her. She said she had been thinking about that and she couldn't conceive of any words helping her. I asked her to think a little bit more. There really ought to be some words in the vocabulary, in the dictionary. I pointed out that I had at least seven dictionaries available in the office. There ought to be some words that could help her. I mentioned the seven dictionaries merely to distract her attention. Why would anyone have seven dictionaries? I named several of them.

Pointing to one I stated:

"This is a dictionary which was given to me by the family of a cancer patient who had suffered intense pain and who had died, but who had lived the last three months of his life with freedom from pain."

I said I had enjoyed working with that particular doctor who had the cancer, and that I had enjoyed using hypnosis with him. I had enjoyed teaching him not to have pain. It hadn't really been too much of a job because he had been very attentive, very interested in this matter of being free of pain.

I had enjoyed working with this patient and teaching him to be free of pain. Now, that particular emphasis on freedom of pain was something I was saying to *this* patient, right here and now, yet I seemed to be talking about the doctor who had died from cancer. *You talk to patients and you space your words, you alter your intonation, so that their unconscious minds separate out the various phrases that you want them to apply to themselves.* It really hadn't been difficult, not difficult at all, for the doctor to learn to close his eyes. To close one's eyes is a very simple thing. Anybody can do it. Even I, even you. Close your eyes. And I kept on in that sort of fashion, and very shortly, Mrs. Jones' eyes closed and she was listening to me.

My suggestion was that there were a number of things about her that interested me. I was interested in freeing her from pain.

> "I really would like to see you free of pain, learning how to control your pain. Really learning how to control your pain."

Notice that first I said *learning*. Next I said *learning how to control pain*. Two different phrases—*learning*, and then *learning how to control*—and she heard both suggestion. Yet I was still talking about the doctor.

> *Rossi:* Erickson is interspersing his therapeutic suggestions for pain control within the general context of his story about the doctor; this generates a "yes set" for accepting Erickson's suggestions to her.[7]

I continued talking in that fashion to her:

> "It isn't really necessary to go to sleep to be free of pain. Why should you go to sleep when you can be free of pain?"

I hope all of you are listening to all the different intonations. And as she continued to listen to me, she went deeper and deeper into a trance. I said it wasn't really necessary, but that means *you can go right ahead and do it even though it isn't necessary*. There is no law against it. It isn't really necessary, but there is no law against it. Go ahead . . . there is no law against it. She developed a very satisfactory trance, and I talked about relaxation and the comfort of muscles, because when one sleeps, muscles tend to relax. There is an alteration of blood supply, an alteration in one's awareness, in one's total capacity to feel; and it is so nice to feel comfort, and it is very nice to feel comfort.

176

It was perfectly obvious that as I talked to Mrs. Jones, she was going deeper and deeper into a trance state and she was feeling comfort. I mentioned to her that time is a variable thing.

"Time can be long and it can be short—very short, unbelievably short, shorter than it is possible to believe. It is very nice to have time be so short, so unbelievably short, especially when you have pain. It is very nice to have time be so short that pain doesn't even have a chance to begin; it doesn't begin at all. It doesn't."

I am overly exaggerating here for your benefit, because a person's unconscious mind tends to listen and tends to single out those things. Any six-month-old baby can look at Mother's face as Mother spoons some pablum toward the baby, and Baby reads the great big headlines on the mother's face: *Who on earth could stand the taste of that stuff?* And the baby agrees and spits it out. So you teach the infants that way. When you deal with patients, *you put the great big headlines on your face,* if their eyes are open; and you put the great big headlines in your voice [if their eyes are closed]. You use certain words for those headlines, and their unconscious minds are just as intelligent at age 50 as they were at age six months.

Indirect Approaches to Pain Control and Weight Loss

Reading Facial Cues in Phrasing Suggestions: Letting 100 Calories "Stick to the Plate"

I spent an hour with Mrs. Jones and then I suggested:

"Three short breaths can take place, and then you can open your eyes."

I waited for the three short breaths. She opened her eyes and then I said to her:

> "You really ought to tell me something about your pain, if you can feel it."

She looked at me in such a surprised fashion and said: "But I don't feel it." I had said,

> "*If you feel it*, you really ought to tell me something about your pain, *if you feel it*."

She was tremendously astounded because she didn't feel pain. Then I continued:

> "They sent you over from the hospital in an ambulance, loaded you in the wheel chair, and brought you into the office here for me to do something about your pain, and you say you haven't got pain?"

She told me that she didn't have pain and that she was as puzzled as could be.

> "But you didn't have your shot," I said. "You had your shot four hours ago, before they loaded you into the ambulance. It is only two minutes drive over here, and you haven't had your shot here. Ordinarily you would have had it on the hour, yet you don't feel pain, do you?"

And I discussed that with her, following the expression on her face for the cues signalling the particular phrases I would use. We talked for some minutes more, and then I made mention to her that I would see her in a week's time, because just looking at me, just discussing this matter of pain, would relieve her pain and make her totally unaware of the fact that the whole hour had passed. Really, a whole week could pass and she ought to be free of pain for that whole week, just as she was right then. She really ought to be free of pain for the whole week. I concluded:

> "I will be glad to see you in a week's time because *there are some other things that I want to see you about.*"

What does that mean, *I want to see you about other things?* It means: *I don't need to see you about pain; I need to see you about other things.* Pain is a matter of the past.

She returned to the hospital, very much confused about the fact that she had been in my office and that she knew very well she had been there only a few minutes, during which time I had said very few words. I had said nothing important, in fact. Essentially, I did no more than tell her I would see her about *other things.* Back at the hospital, she got no more medication that day, slept soundly that night, and got no medication the next morning. The next evening she stated to the nurse: "I think my pain might return. Would you give me a prophylactic dose (a shot)? But I don't think it will take as much." The nurse gave her either a quarter grain of morphine or 100mg. of Demerol but not the combination of both, and the patient slept soundly that night.

In the morning the patient said: "I had a nice night's sleep, and I would like to have a nice day today. You know, I have been taking medication every four hours for two months because of my pain—my very real pain—and I don't want it to return and I don't want to be a dope addict. Will I be a drug addict if I have two shots a day, if I need them?"

"You can have a shot whenever you want one," the nurse answered. The patient responded, "Well, I will take one in the morning and one at night, and I will see how much of a craving I have for it." So she got her morning shot. Then in the evening her statement was: "I don't have the craving, but somewhere in me I feel a certain kind of weakness and I think maybe my pain will return because of that weakness." It was very nice wording, and so she got her evening injection.

The next day the question arose: Could she take the dose of medication by mouth instead of by injection? So they gave her an anti-pain pill. The doctor told me that they had reduced her medication. I told him I didn't want to know what kind of medication she was being given for the simple reason that I didn't want to convey to the patient that I really knew anything at all about the medication. I didn't think it was important for me to know about the medication. I am a doctor, and if I don't think it is important to know about the medication, the medication in itself must not be important. The patient became interested in finding out if she could get along on that reduced medication for 24 hours. Yes, she could, but at the end of 24 hours the pain was becoming increasingly strong, so she decided to take the medication at the end of 24 hours. Then she said, "Maybe I'll sleep better if I take a pill." So morning and night, she takes a pill. But sometimes she forgets.

On the occasion of her second visit, I raised the question of her weight.

"Even in the hospital for 13 weeks on an 800-calories diet, you still weigh 255 pounds, and you cannot reduce. I wonder if you could let 100 calories stick to the plate? It ought to be interesting and amusing to look at 100 calories sticking to a plate. And how are you going to feel when you see those calories sticking to your plate? It ought to be an amusing thing. How are you going to visualize it? What shape are they going to be in? Are they going to be flat, round, square, with corners, angles—those calories that stick to the plate?"

Treating Epilepsy with Suggestion

Paradoxical Symptom Prescription: Having Minor Convulsions to Avoid Major Seizures

I also said:

"You know, I have never seen your epileptic seizure. I think I am entitled to see at least one. And I really am entitled to see one. I have seen epileptic seizures before and I know what they are like. I don't think we have to put all the adornments, all the trimmings, on the epileptic seizure, because I am more interested in muscle behavior—the tonic and the clonic seizures—the convulsive manifestations. Where do they first begin?"

Her statement was: "I feel rather funny and then my right hand starts to quiver, and then I don't seem to know anything at all."

I watched a minor convulsive seizure and it lasted about three minutes. It was a rather minor one. When she came out of it I asked her immediately: "Do you feel rather relaxed?"

"Yes."

"Tired?"

"Yes."

"It is a good thing to feel tired and relaxed and comfortable after a seizure," I said. "Isn't that enough to feel? I think it is. I think anybody can be satisfied to feel relaxed and tired and comfortable after an epileptic seizure. So let's talk for a few minutes about the weather, Viet Nam, or something about Phoenix, or anything else. And after a few minutes, see if you can have another convulsion."

That is exactly what she did. She had another convulsion. And she had the second, and the third, and the fourth convulsion under exactly the same circumstances. I had suggested she have another convulsion. Now, why would I do that? I needed to give her practice in having minor convulsions instead of major convulsions. I pointed out to her how very nice it was to have had those convulsions—and having had four in my office really ought to suffice for a day or two. I didn't know what the requisite number of convulsions were for a week. She said it had been about two a day. That is why she spent her day either in bed or sitting in a wheel chair, because she didn't want to be standing up—for when you fall in an epileptic seizure, you are likely to hurt yourself very severely. Her statement that you are likely to hurt yourself very severely is another nice description of her epileptic seizures and their realities. "You are likely to hurt yourself very severely."

She had very few seizures that week, and she lost one-and-a-half pounds from the calories that stuck to her plate. In four weeks she lost seven-in-a-half pounds, which is a fairly good loss of weight, and she is still continuing to lose weight. I have reduced her convulsions very greatly. Usually, a doctor does not suggest to a patient that the patient *have convulsions*. But why shouldn't you suggest it? When you suggest the convulsions, the body isn't ready; there has not been a buildup of whatever forces are to be discharged. You are potentiating an early discharge of energy, and so you are going to get a minor convulsion. When you get a minor convulsion, the patient's body learns how to have minor convulsions. In four-weeks' time she has had only one major convulsion. It happened when she was walking across the room, and she fell and hurt herself. She is now aware of the fact that it is better to sit down in the chair and let a minor convulsion occur.

> "You blank out when your right arm starts quivering, and it really isn't necessary to feel that weak, but you can feel comfortable after the convulsion, but you don't have to feel weak. Just feel comfortable and relaxed."

At most, she has one or two very minor convulsions a day, at an hour of her own choice.

Telephone Hypnosis: Jokes in Trance

Steady Weight Loss; the Unconscious Mind as Straight-forward and Honest; Utilizing Doubt and a Behavioral Inevitability to "Go into Trance after Hanging up the Phone"

What has happened to her pain? She still has the pain. She

182

wonders when she will lose enough weight to allow her to undergo an operation. The orthopedic surgeon is becoming more interested in her. The doctor who had been studying her peculiar metabolic disturbance that allowed her to maintain her weight of 255 pounds on an 800-calorie diet is beginning to wonder what is involved in that sort of a physiological condition. What is that metabolic disturbance that somebody else—a psychiatrist—is suggesting the sticking of calories to a plate and effecting a loss of weight?

During my last interview with her in the office, I wondered if she could let 150 calories stick to her plate, and if she did, she could have all of the remaining 650 calories.

> "Just let a mere 150 calories stick to your plate—just a mere 150. You can have all the remaining 650, and it is easy to let calories stick to the plate."

I was still asking whether they were round, or square, or angular. What shape were those calories, really? A ridiculous question? How many of us really appreciate the childishness of the unconscious mind? *The unconscious mind is decidedly simple and unaffected. It is straightforward and honest.* It hasn't got all of the veneer of what we call adult culture. It is rather simple, rather childish. I like to joke with my patients in the trance state—rather simple jokes, rather childish jokes.

I have had two telephone calls from her, because I pointed out to her that coming to my office is a rather expensive thing.

> "I think it is much better for you to call me up on the hour, about five minutes before the hour, and listen to me explain a few things to you. And I will do it very briefly so that you can hang up the receiver before you go into a trance. So be sure you are sitting comfortably in a chair when you call me up, and be very sure that it is a comfortable chair, so that you can hang up the receiver before you go into a trance."

Why all that emphasis on hanging up the receiver before

she goes into a trance? *There is no doubt that she is going into a trance; the only doubt is about hanging up the receiver.* That is where I want the doubts to be. Will she manage to hang up the receiver? So far, she has managed to hang up the receiver. The first time over the phone I suggested that she have a 15-minute trance, "but longer if you think it is necessary." The telephone disturbed her by ringing after 40 minutes, and her statement to me when she reported it was: "Apparently, I needed 40 minutes, and I really felt so good." Now I have suggested that merely touching the receiver on the telephone will be sufficient, and maybe it will be necessary for her to make only one visit a month while the calories (150 or maybe 200) stick to the plate. So, I am waiting to see what is going to happen there.

Here was a fearful, cooperative, honest patient, wrapped in anxiety, very much concerned about her sciatic pain, very much concerned about her weight; very much concerned by the fact that the orthopedic surgeon considered her a poor surgical risk, the fact that the internist felt she could not reduce because of metabolic disturbances of an unknown character. How did she manage to reduce? This matter of 100 calories sticking to the plate—what sort of a view does that woman have of her plate? How does she see it? How does she see her food? How does she get that feeling of satiety when she eats around 700 calories? Food *does* stick to her plate. She doesn't feel the need to scrape her plate clean. I am wondering how long will it be necessary for me to have her call me up? How long will it be necessary for me to have her make a monthly visit? I know I have her epilepsy under control. She did have that one serious, major convulsion when she fell. She thinks she was careless walking across the room—that she should have made provisions for a minor seizure. Now, how can one really control major epilepsy in which the EEG shows the proper spiking for idiopathic epilepsy? That isn't the only epileptic patient to whom I have suggested minor convulsions, because they can have minor convulsions. It isn't really necessary to soil themselves, wet themselves.

I think a great deal of research ought to be done, and I don't think I should be the only one to do it. I think some of the people in this audience ought to do some of that research.

Conscious Vs. Unconscious Communication (Minimal Cues)

The Illusion of a Well-Adjusted Personality:
Suspecting a Chain-Smoker's Request for Cure;
Anxiety Underlying Chronic Habits

One woman came to see me, and I have never seen a more well-adjusted person in my life. She was alert, likable, her responses were interesting, and she had a good daily routine. Her entire history was excellent, except that she smoked four packs of cigarettes a day! Her statement was that she had come to see me to have that habit corrected. I asked her why she wanted the habit corrected. She said that every time she started to cut down on her smoking, she became cross, irritable, disagreeable, and offensive in her behavior. But if she smoked a cigarette, she would become her ordinary, smiling, helpful, cooperative, friendly, agreeable self.

She developed a trance very easily, and then I asked her the same questions again, and she again gave the same answer. I asked her if there was any other reason for seeing me, and she stated that there was no other reason. *I suggested that she smoke only that number of cigarettes that she found necessary.* She was utterly delighted. She came back the next day, stating:

"When I left here, I had the feeling that I had not been hypnotized, that you had just talked to me. I heard everything you said. It seemed to me that I just closed my eyes. I do know that when I was here in the office, several times I started to take a cigarette—but the look in your face stopped me. Then I left here. I wondered all the way home when I would take another cigarette. I wondered if I would take one after lunch. I did. And I wondered all afternoon if I would take another. I took one after dinner, and I haven't smoked any today. I might smoke one after lunch today. I might smoke one after dinner today, but I am down to a few cigarettes from four packs a day. I have been smoking four packs a day for a couple of years, so I think you had better have another session with me and take me off those two cigarettes."

I asked her to go into a trance, and this time she went into a trance wherein she had no doubts about it at all. Again I told her that she could smoke that number of cigarettes that she considered desirable, but this time *she ought to smoke them informatively—that is, if she did smoke.* She phoned me very early the next morning, before I had gotten out of bed, to tell me that she wanted to come in immediately.

It wasn't a well-adjusted woman who came in to see me that morning. It was a beautiful picture of anxiety and fear! She was tremulous, and the muscles of her face were twitching. She said: "I know there is nothing wrong with me, but look at me. I am in a horrible state of nerves. What did I do yesterday? I sneaked two cigarettes. I lied to my husband, I lied to everybody, I lied to my children, but I can't lie to myself. I sneaked those cigarettes, and I didn't want to smoke them. I had no desire to smoke them, and yet I did, and with each puff I felt a tremendous amount of anxiety and sneakiness, and I am utterly, completely frightened. What have I been covering up?"

I mention this case (I have only seen her three times now) for the simple reason that she came in presenting such a beautiful appearance, and her history was so excellent. She said she had only a bad habit of smoking four packs of cigarettes. Her husband didn't smoke, she didn't drink, and he didn't drink. There were no bad habits. They did not watch the television too much, the two children were well-adjusted—everything was fine. I couldn't see any reason in the world why she should come in and ask me to help her stop smoking cigarettes. That is why I asked her to smoke only that number of cigarettes that was necessary, and so she smoked the two. Then she came back and wanted to get rid of smoking altogether, and I told her to smoke that number of cigarettes that she considered desirable, but to smoke them *informatively.*

Now, in our third interview, she tells me her first husband

186

was an alcoholic, and so was she. She had two children by him. The older one was living with him and the younger one was living with her. She is certain the older child is going to go to the dogs, but she is not particularly concerned because the child was a behavior problem from the very beginning, and he doesn't want to live with her anyway. The second child does want to live with her. And she has a daughter by her second husband.

She knows she has some kind of an anxiety problem; she knows that she is afraid to face it; she is wondering what it is in her attitude toward her children, toward her husband, toward everything. What is it she has been hiding behind those four packs of cigarettes a day? She is very, very convinced that she is hiding something. She is an extremely anxious person. She also said that going back to four packs of cigarettes isn't going to be any relief anymore. "I've got no real interest in smoking cigarettes. What I want to know is, what have I been covering up all this time? I *have* been covering up something. My husband has laughed at me for doing that amount of smoking; he has laughed at me for cleaning up the ashtrays regularly."

When patients come to you and ask you to remove or cure a habit such as chain smoking, I think you ought to become exceedingly suspicious.

Unconscious Vs. Conscious Communication

Recognizing Minimal Cues in Vocal Tones;
Sexual Incompatibility Covering Fear of Aging

A husband and wife came to see me, explaining that they had been married for seven years, and that although they were very much in love with each other, they were having marital problems. Their marital problems all related to sex. They could not agree on frequency or duration. This problem had been developing slowly over the past three years. She has resented sex; he has been oversexed. Otherwise, their lives had been very happy, very agreeable. He is successful in his business; she has been working; they have two children; they are getting their home paid for; they don't want their marriage broken up. And they kept on discussing this matter of their sexual adjustment.

Finally, I asked them to give me their ages. Remember, they had been married for seven years. She gave her age as 24; he gave his age as 28. Then I sent him out of the office and told her I wanted to talk to her.

"How old did you say you were?" I asked. Unfortunately, I cannot duplicate the exact way in which she answered. She said "24" with a very peculiar emphasis and in a most remarkable way. The *24* was clear: you could hear it, you could understand it, you knew it was 24, but she looked puzzled.

"Do you know that you are very badly frightened?" I asked.

"No, I certainly don't know that," she responded. "The only thing that is troubling me is my marriage, and I don't want that broken up."

"But I think you are badly frightened," I persisted.

"I think there are going to be two more times when you are going to be badly frightened. Two more times."

"But I am not frightened now," she answered. "What on earth do you mean?"

"Fright, fear. You are scared to death," I said.

She looked me over, and she looked me over, and then she said: "I haven't the slightest idea what you mean."

"I will help you out," I responded.

"I will tell you the last time you will be very badly frightened. You are going to be frightened like this once again, and then once again. The third time will be when you are age 39 or 40."

"My father died when he was 42," she said, "and when I get out of my twenties, all my life will be behind me."

When she says goodbye to her twenties, all of her life is

going to be behind her. When she reaches her forties, when she reaches her menopause, she is going to be completely through with life.

I didn't know about the death of her father at age 42, but I did know that when she gave me her age as 24, I didn't like the sound of her voice. It had a frightened tone to it, an exceedingly frightened tone. I just didn't like it. I did a little arithmetic: she was married at 17 and she was now 24. In another year, she would be a quarter of a century old. How many of you appreciate that unconscious reaction that women have about being not *25, but a quarter of a century old?* There is that awful fear of leaving behind them, forever, their twenties. They just don't want to leave behind their twenties and to enter into their thirties; and their forties is another crucial time.

As she recognized the significance of what I meant by being frightened again at the age of 39 or 40, and specified that her father had died when he was 42, her entire physical appearance changed. Up to that time, I had been seeing a woman about 5 feet 7 1/2 inches tall, sitting upright in a chair. When she stated that she would leave behind most of her life (really, *all* of her life) when she left her twenties, everything about her physical movements and facial appearance presented the picture of a very, very, very badly scared little girl, cowering in a great big chair.

Then I asked her, "What has been happening recently?"

"Well," she began, "I feel that I've missed everything by marrying so early in my life. I didn't have any girlhood; I didn't have any young womanhood. My oldest child is six years old. I was suddenly confronted with being an old married woman with a baby. Now I am an old married woman with *two* children, and that is all I am. I am scared because I will be a quarter of a century old, just as you said, but I wouldn't face it. I have known this was coming ever since I was 21 and reached my majority."

When she turned 21 and became an adult (legally), her marital problems began—that was three years ago. I called her husband in and I told the two of them they were not to discuss what had taken place unless they wanted to. The next morning

I got a special delivery letter stating: "We have had a long, long discussion. We didn't tell you that we had been to see several other psychiatrists, and we didn't like anything about those psychiatrists. We told them we had marital problems and they tried to help us out. You listened, but you didn't think our marital problems were the important problems. My wife is certain that you can help her, and so we want the earliest possible appointment with you. My wife will come in to see you until she can really talk freely."

When patients come to you, they will hide their anxieties very carefully, in spite of the fact that they have come to see you. These particular people had gone to see several other psychiatrists about their marital problems. For three years, he has been oversexed and she has been undersexed. She would rather he didn't touch her ever again. They were married when she was 17. They had had premarital sexual relations for nine months on the average of four times a week; they had been having sexual relations three years ago between three to five times a week; and all of a sudden, three years ago, their sexual relations just dropped off. There was that peculiar tone of voice in which she said she was 24 years old—just the pronunciation of that one word was the important clue.

Patients do come to you with tremendous anxieties, and it is all-important that you recognize their anxiety. You ought not to be led astray by this question of marital problems; by this question of smoking four packs of cigarettes. Why do patients have psychiatric problems? It is because they do not want to face them. Why do they have anxiety problems? Because they do not want to face the problems they have, and that is why it becomes necessary for you to be willing to point up certain things. They want you to understand the things they do not know consciously that they are depending upon you to understand. *Consciously*, they will tell you any story that seems to be reasonable, that seems to be well-founded, and they will tell it to you with great intensity. They will make you believe it, but they are using that particular story.

The patient who smoked four packs of cigarettes dropped down to two cigarettes and came in to tell me so happily about it. When I told her to call me up in a month's time, I got that worried, anxious, fearful call the next morning from her. It just hadn't seemed reasonable to me. There was something in the way she told me about the four packs of cigarettes, just as when the other woman told me her age with a note in her voice that was like a red flag.

Too often, physicians overlook the meaningfulness of communication. They are listening to words, to stories, to general accounts, and not listening to the actual communication that the patient is offering. *The actual communication concerns the things that the patient is too afraid to face and is too unwilling to face.* That is why professional help is being sought. The fact that there had been previous psychiatrists to whom they had told the same story didn't come out until afterwards. I usually do not take a complete history in the first session because I want to listen to that first presentation that the patient offers. I didn't think the four packs of cigarettes was a true story. As far as cigarettes were concerned, it was true; as far as the patient was concerned, four packs of cigarettes was the entire story; but it didn't seem that way to me. She was so happy on the second day of her success, and she wrote me a check so happily. When I told her to call me in about a month's time to let me know how she was getting along, I was wondering how many days it would take her to wake up to the fact that she had something else to communicate to me. I knew that she was going to call me very soon; I knew that it wouldn't be a month or two, but that it would be very soon.

I cite these two cases as excellent instances of the need to listen to patients always, and to form your own conclusions from what you notice, from what you see, from what you understand, and never to take your patient's word for anything. I frequently tell my patients:

"I never believe anything that I hear from that chair over there until I have confirmed and reaffirmed it. It is interesting to listen to, but you should not believe it until you really know."

That sort of an attitude toward your patients is utterly important, not only in psychiatry, but also in medicine and dentistry.

Conscious Vs. Unconscious Communication (Minimal Cues)

Dental (Jaw) Problem Disguised as School Problem: Concealed Feelings

I can think of a 15-year-old patient whose statement to me concerned her difficulties in school. She didn't like her teachers. She found that she didn't like to be a grade grubber; she just didn't like that kind of studying, and that was her complaint. Her parents sent her to me because they said that she was far brighter than her marks were indicating. I kept listening as the girl talked to me, and I kept asking her, "What are the things that you are not telling me?"

Finally she told me, "Well, I don't like my dentist." I asked her why. "Because he never says anything about my chin."

"What about your chin?" I asked.

"I don't like my chin," she answered.

"Tell me about your chin."

"It's too heavy," she began, "and my lower teeth are beginning to stick out in front of my upper teeth."

I sent her to tell her dentist that particular complaint, and he sent her to an orthodontist. The orthodontist examined her very, very carefully and called in a couple of other orthodontists, and it was determined that she needed a jaw operation because her mandible was protruding.

Now, what did that girl do to conceal that complaint from her dentist? How did she behave? It seems to me that a dentist would notice that kind of a problem. Was he careless? Was the girl so gay, so happy, and contented that he failed to notice? I didn't like her story about her grades. I didn't like anything at all about her story. It was an unconvincing narrative, and I kept asking her about the things that she didn't want to tell me. Then she told me it was her dentist whom she didn't like. How did she conceal her feelings from her dentist? Yet, I do know that patients will conceal their feelings.

Perceiving Patients' Unconscious Distractions

Sneezing Fits to Divert Physician's Attention from Breast Exam; A Master Pickpocket

I can think of the patient who came to see me and said: "During the past three years I have been going to one doctor after another. I have been hospitalized. I have been given very careful examinations. I have told every one of the doctors about my food intolerances and about my history of pelvic infection when I was a girl. They have done very careful studies of me. I have been hospitalized for a week at a time, about ten times. I have been given physical examinations by 26 different physicians from the top of my head to the soles of my feet, and yet I am unsatisfied."

"Why are you coming to see a psychiatrist?" I asked. "I am not going to do a physical examination on you, and you know that."

"I know you aren't," she answered.

I summarized:

"You have had physical examinations by 26 different physicians. You have been hospitalized, had your liver studied, had your pelvis studied; and you talk about your girlhood infection. Yet you are telling me, a psychiatrist, about all this. It looks to me as if you are awfully anxious about something, because who would go to see 26 different physicians and be hospitalized repeatedly for a week at a time with innumerable laboratory studies? You would have to be an anxious patient.

"Now, as you think over all the physical examinations you have had, tell me what one peculiar thing you did during the examinations."

193

She looked at me and asked, "What peculiar thing?"

"I don't know," I said, "but it seems to me you must have done a peculiar thing to distract all those doctors' attention."

"I always have a sneezing fit when the doctor examines my right breast," she answered, "so he never does examine it." My response was:

"All right, I will call up the surgeon right now. You started those physical examinations three years ago, and you have had a sneezing fit every time the physician touched your right breast. That distracts his attention. What is it about your right breast?"

"There is a lump in the lower part of it, deep in it," she answered.

"So, the doctor does a superficial examination of your right breast. You know about that lump; you have had it for three years, you have a sneezing fit, and you don't tell the doctor about. I will send you to Dr. X."

A few hours later Dr. X called me back and said, "I have hospitalized her. I am doing a radical mastectomy tomorrow morning." Yes, she had a carcinoma with metastases to the axilla.

When a patient does a peculiar thing, when a patient gives a peculiar history, I think you ought to be very, very curious about it. Anxiety will show itself, and you ought to be able to recognize it: 26 physicians, a dozen week-long hospitalizations, innumerable laboratory studies, that narrative of frequent pelvic disease when she was a girl, some food intolerances (but no prescriptions), no diagnosis of liver disease or gall bladder disease. Why would she see that number of physicians in three years' time? The average person does well to have a physical examination every year. The entire history is suspicious in itself. You ought to be concerned about it. There is something compulsive about it; something that signifies tremendous anxiety.

What can people do to distract your attention? I can think of an entertainer who was a pickpocket. He could take a man's suspenders off him; he could take his belt off him while the man was standing on the stage in front of the audience. I got acquainted with the man. I sat down at a little narrow table and said, "I have my coat buttoned. I've got certain objects in my shirt pocket, and I am going to be watching you. I am a trained observer, and I really want to see what you are going to do about those things in my shirt pocket."

We had a delightful discussion, and I talked to him and he talked to me about this matter of observing others, about distracting attention, and finally he said: "Well, Doctor, here is your pencil," and he handed me the things I had placed in my shirt pocket. My coat was still buttoned. I don't know when he did it; I was watching him the entire time, and I am very good at observation. But he was very good at distraction, also!

Utilizing Verbal Violence in Direct Authoritative Hypnosis

When patients come for therapy, you ought to be aware of the fact that they cannot face certain things, and they are going to distract you. They may distract you because they are anxious and resistant, as I have described in the previous cases, or because they are manifesting another type of resistance. I had a patient who came in the doorway of my office and announced: "Well, here I am! I telephoned you from San Francisco. I told you I wanted to come, and you gave me an appointment at this time. Here I am, but I don't like the looks of you. I don't want to be your patient!"

"But you are here," I answered.

The patient responded with a string of profanities.

"All right," I said. "Shut up! Sit down in that chair there and go into a trance!"

And the patient did.

Why did this person come all the way from San Francisco to see me? Why shouldn't I recognize that the patient wanted violence when the patient started swearing at me from the threshold of my office? Why shouldn't I offer back a violence of an acceptable kind?

Language Retraining in Brain Injury Cases

Not Pushing Patients before They Are Ready

Question: In cases where brain injury has occurred, we have been trained to begin language retraining work with patients as soon as they can tolerate it. You have commented, however, that one should wait until the brain heals. Would you please elaborate?

Answer: I know that there are two schools of thought on the subject of retraining brain-injured patients. My feeling is that it is very much like toilet training in children. Some mothers will force toilet training on children very, very early. Then they discover that the child has grown older and has suddenly lost all of that training; now he needs to go through yet another learning period.

One ought to train a child on the toilet at a time when the child is ready to learn. If you toilet train a child before he has learned to recognize the sensations of pelvic pressure, then as soon as he learns the sensations of pelvic pressure, he will lose the previous toilet training. Then the training has to be completely repeated.

In cases of brain injury you retrain patients to speak, depending on where the injury is located in the brain. If you begin retraining before the brain has healed, you get the first healing but then you get the alterations that occur as the lymph tissues begin to harden and become firm. The first healing of the skin in surgery is of a certain character, and then it changes and becomes somewhat different. I think it is the same way with the brain.

I recently met a boy who had been very badly injured in an automobile accident last June. His doctors had begun speech therapy on him very shortly thereafter (in August). When I saw the boy in February and listened to him talking and observed his writing, I felt that it had been a very serious mistake to have begun the speech therapy so soon after the accident. So I had the father discontinue the speech therapy.

When the boy had been off the therapy for about a month, I called up the father (they lived in Illinois) and asked how the boy was getting along. The father responded: "During all those months my son was doing speech therapy, his speech seemed to improve but other areas seemed to be slipping. He was becoming increasingly paranoid, increasingly suspicious, increasingly fanatical about religious matters. Everything seemed to be going wrong; he even had a compulsion to write letters to the president. Since you have taken him off the speech therapy, and reduced his activity as much as possible, he has lost his paranoid tendency, he has lost his religiosity, he has been much more agreeable, and he has not been obsessed with listening to the same record on the record player all day long."

In other words, the boy has responded very positively. Over the phone he was able to tell me that he was glad I had taken him off speech therapy. At first he had been disappointed and resentful, but now he felt so much better, and he didn't feel so pushed.

PART V

Creative Choice With Therapeutic Double Binds[1]

Therapeutic Reorientation via the Double Bind

Structuring Double Binds to Redirect Aggression in the Treatment of a Patient with Cerebral Palsy: "Your Fanny Is Fat Enough"

In therapeutic hypnosis you use the double bind in a wealth of ways. You can use it, not only to get patients to face the important issues, but also to confront them with a reorientation. For example:

> "Why must you have your headache on weekends?"

Why not give patients the double bind of having a middle-of-the-week headache to reorient them? In this matter of phobias, why not give the patient a double bind on his phobia such that he will be particularly afraid of high buildings that are painted *red?* You are giving him a double bind:

> "You've got to look for a *red* building in order to have the most acute phobia."

You see, the double bind works in a variety of ways. Sometimes you use it to reorient patients in their thinking.

What is the purpose of hypnosis but to present new and different ideas so that patients can alter their ways of thinking? We deal with patients in a frank, matter-of-fact way. I can think of the university student with cerebral palsy who entered my office and sat down in the chair. Promptly, those uncoordinated movements of her palsied left arm and foot became apparent. I let her wave her left arm and foot while I took her history. It didn't take very long to find out that she was very much concerned about being a homely girl, and very much concerned about being overweight. However, she believed implicitly in her own intelligence, and she knew that she could get a doctoral degree.

I began by agreeing with her that she could have a doctoral degree; that she was homely; and that she was overweight. Next, she mentioned that she was also horribly aggressive, and I agreed that she was horribly aggressive. As soon as I had her personality sized up in what I thought was an adequate fashion, I pointed out that there was no need for that aggressive waving of her arm and leg. Her fanny was fat enough to park on her hand, so that she didn't have to wave it around in the air. Why shouldn't I do it that way? Then I pointed out that the right leg was also fat enough to park on top of her left thigh, and hold her left leg down aggressively.

Now, *I* defined aggression there. I did not ask her to *stop* being aggressive. I created a double bind in which she had to continue the aggression. In fact, she *needed* to be aggressive because of the [offensive but frank] way I had spoken to her. Theoretically, it was wrong of me to speak that way. She just looked at me and glared. Then she parked her left hand under her hip, and she crossed her legs and held her left leg still.

"Now you're using aggression usefully," I told her. "Keep right on using aggression usefully, and you can expect me to further stimulate aggressiveness on your part."

She got her doctoral degree. Several years later she took me out to dinner in a restaurant. It was very interesting. She walks with a limp, and so do I; but I always had the feeling that she was more handicapped, physically, than I. But the waiter helped me off with my overcoat and ignored the lady. He was really thoughtful of me. She and I laughed at her ability to handle her handicap—and to handle me—in such a way that she directed the waiter's attention toward me and away from herself. It was a perfectly beautiful interaction.

How did I work with her? I structured that double bind by asked her to use aggression, by putting her in a situation in which she had to be aggressive, and by creating a situation that proved a need for still further aggression. I think all of you ought to take time out to work on this question of a double bind, and to recognize how many times it is used.

Everyday Applications of the Double Bind

Salesman's Tricks: Converting Resistance into Acceptance

There is the salesman who wants you to sign on the dotted line. He extends paper and pencil to you, and then says, "Oh, no, use a pen." You refuse to sign with a pencil, which obligates you to sign with a pen. He has given you a chance to refuse to sign, and you exercised it; but here you find a pen in your hand, which requires you to sign.

I can recall the consternation of the salesman who pulled that gag on me. I said, "That's right, I don't want to sign with a pencil." Then I looked at that nice, beautiful, anticipatory expression on his face and added, "And I don't want to sign with a pen either!" Then I discussed that double bind with him. He didn't call it a double bind; he just thought it was part of his training technique.

Another double bind: "Oh, that X is in the wrong place—it should be up here." So you don't sign where the X is in the wrong place, you sign where the X is in the right place—a double bind. It is very neat, very gentle, and very effective.

Ethical Use of the Double Bind

*Misusing a Non-Therapeutic Double-Double Bind
to the Therapist's Advantage*

All of you ought to consider this matter of the double bind as a method of getting your patient to face the issues at hand. *But you always structure the double bind to the advantage of the patient, not to your own advantage.* Whenever you put a patient in a double bind to your advantage—by saying, for example, "Of course, I could see you tomorrow afternoon or Friday, *but tomorrow afternoon is my golf day"* —then you are really putting the patient in a double-*double* bind. He'll see you on Friday, but he is very likely to find a physician who doesn't put him in a double-double bind.

"I could see you Thursday or Friday, but I suppose Friday would be the more convenient day for you." Well, you'd better take your chances. You offered Friday as the more convenient day, but the patient finds that Thursday is the more convenient day. Play golf on Friday, but don't ask in that way. Are there any questions on the double bind?

Rossi: This section as well as the previous one illustrate how *not* to use the double bind. The basic principle for the ethical use of the double bind always involves the patient's advantage—never that of the therapist or some other party. More details on the ethical use of the double bind are presented in Part VII of this volume.

The Double Bind in the Treatment of Frigidity and Premature Ejaculation

*Time-Binding Suggestions, Confusion, and the Paradoxical
Use of Pathological Mechanisms; Reversing Obsessive-
Compulsive Behaviors*

[*Question from the audience concerns female sexual*

dysfunction and premature ejaculation.]

One double bind I use on women who are orgasmically dysfunctional is this:

> "Now, listen. You are a young woman, and you've got a long life ahead of you. I think you ought to learn everything possible about your genital sensations. Actually, I really hope that *you won't have an orgasm before you've learned all the sensations.* In fact, it seems to me that even if you are unusually rapid in learning, it is going to take you three months. I would like to say six months but, of course, there are also those people who learn very quickly and suddenly in a week's time. Now, I've given you a week, three months, six months—*but please don't learn too soon.*
>
> "What does what I am telling you mean? It means that you are going to learn. There is no doubt, no question about it; *the only thing that you need to worry about is learning too soon.*"

Most of the reactions I've gotten to that approach are to the effect of, too soon is not really soon enough! They feel, "I *can* learn, soon and thoroughly."

In the matter of premature ejaculation, sometimes I will point out:

> "You have had a premature ejaculation for 20 years. You have seen every physician in the United States and you have always come out of the examination with the exact same problem you entered it with: premature ejaculation! Did any one of those physicians you consulted ever think to tell you the eventual outcome of a premature ejaculation? The *eventual* outcome? Sooner or later, *you are going to have that horribly frustrating experience of being unable to ejaculate,* no matter how hard you try. And when that happens, I hope you'll come to me and worry about it with me."

Well, I do hope he does. Patients have come back to worry about it with me, not realizing what they have accomplished. We sit down and worry about it, and I have the opportunity to give them some insights.

What have I done? *I have taken a certain obsessive-compulsive doubt about sex and reversed it.* The patients are using the same mechanisms of expectancy and defeat in relationship to an ejaculation. They have been defeated by their ejaculations, and I have simply taken that reality and continued it as a defeating reality. It is a double bind, you see. They are bound to be defeated by premature ejaculation; they are bound to be defeated by a failure to ejaculate. But they have accomplished something! Then it is an easy matter of teaching:

> "Well, you know, I don't know whether you will have your next ejaculation at ten minutes before the hour, or on the hour; whether you'll have the ejaculation 27 1/2 minutes after beginning sexual relations, or 32 3/4 minutes after beginning relations."

You know, I *don't* know. But why that half minute? Why that three-quarters of a minute? It is just to distract attention. It is a matter of confusion: They cannot think it through, they cannot understand it; but they are bound to keep on worrying about that unessential point. And as they worry about that unessential point, they are accepting the concept of 27 minutes, or 33 minutes, or 47 minutes, or 17 minutes. That is exactly what I want them to accept, so it is a double bind again.

Self-Defeating Patients

Beware of the Self-Defeating Patient; Goal-Setting as the Patient's Prerogative: Accepting a Mediocre Goal

Bear in mind that some of your patients are going to defeat themselves, no matter what on earth you do for them. There

204

are the people who succeed in life despite anything; and there are the people who fail in life despite everything.

I saw a patient recently who had a psychogenic migraine headache, accompanied by a psychogenic depression. He is 38 years old. He has been a very, very devout Catholic since the age of 20. At the age of 20 he decided he wanted to get married and have a home and children. He is now 38 years old, and he has dated hundreds of girls. Of course, his wife has to be Catholic; it has to be a Catholic home, and so forth. He has dated hundreds of girls, but each one turned out to be a Protestant! He hasn't been able to find a Catholic girl.

Now, does that man want to get married? I listened to him explain to me very earnestly his absolute desire to have a Catholic home life, to have Catholic children, to have Catholic devotions in his home. Then I got the rest of his history on the Protestant girls. It took a lot of labor on his part to miss all those Catholic girls, and I told him as much! His response was, "What am I going to do about my belief that I want to marry a Catholic girl?"

"You are rather stuck with it, aren't you?" I answered.

"Don't you think you had better regard those 18 years of regularly dating Protestant girls, one after another, as absolute proof that you do not want a Catholic wife, a Catholic home, Catholic children, Catholic devotions?"

I think he ought to accept 18 years of proof.

What has he done in every other aspect of his living? He did his level best to graduate from college in the lower 10 percent of his class despite his brains, and he succeeded. Whenever he gets a job within his level of competency—as I said, he is a very brilliant chap—he looks over the situation to find what would be the most irritating behavior to his boss. Then he succeeds in doing that very behavior within the first year or 18 months of his employment, so that he gets fired. Sometimes he knows he is going to be discharged at the end of a year; sometimes he knows he's going to be discharged at the end of 18 months. He can pinpoint the period of his discharge. We went over every one of his occupations, his jobs, and it was always the same defeating pattern.

He says he wants a large family to support, a good income, a nice home. But he has years of economic proof that he isn't ever going to have those things, because he is unemployed a good share of the time. Sometimes it takes him three months to get a job, and he never saves more than enough money to tide him over during the next immediate period of unemployment, which he expects to have.

Can you do therapy on this man? Why did he wait for therapy until the age of 38? Why did he try four different psychiatrists, until his family physician said, "Go and see Dr. Erickson." He waited until age 37; now at age 38, he is trying to see me. I'm not going to accept him as a patient. He has demonstrated what he wants. There are those people who insist on failing, just as there are those people who insist on succeeding. There are also those people who insist on mediocrity. When people set therapeutic goals for themselves, you'll find there are those who insist on setting goals of failure; there are those who insist on mediocre therapeutic goals; and there are those who insist on excellent therapeutic goals.

You need to appraise your patient. Never strive for *your* idea of perfection, because you can't force your ideas of perfection upon patients. You offend and wrong patients who want mediocrity in their therapeutic gains when you try to force excellence upon them. You offend and wrong patients who insist upon therapeutic excellence when you ask them to put up with a makeshift therapy. *So you do therapy according to the capacity of the patient to receive it.*

The Price of Pleasing Others

*Treating Gastric Hemorrhage in an
Obsessive-Compulsive Man: "Take to the Hills"
to Learn Self-Satisfaction in Non-essential Tasks*

I can think of a certain patient to illustrate my point. He was 21 years old, and all his life he had done things *only* to please his parents. At the age of 14 I had looked him over and thought, "Poor devil. I wonder when you're going to get your stomach ulcer, because you're predestined to get one." I wondered what I could say to his parents. Eventually, I did try to say a few things to them, but it was useless. They knew more about the wonderful qualities of their son than I did!

At the age of 21, the young man had a severe gastric hemorrhage. I think he had a total of six transfusions while he was hospitalized. I saw him shortly thereafter. He had so much tension, anxiety, and distress that his future looked utterly hopeless. I can assure you, it was literally painful to sit there and talk to that chap. Usually I relax and sit back in my chair, letting my patients have their own tensions. But this boy's tensions were horrible!

Nevertheless, I outlined a course of therapy for him: Give up that obsessive-compulsive desire to finish his university work; give up that obsessive-compulsive desire to work and save money. He is the kind of a chap who, if he saved $10 one week, he would mourn and regret and be distressed that it wasn't $10.25. And if he did save $10.25, he would feel it should have been $10.50. He had that chronic, total, absolute dissatisfaction with himself.

In my outline of his therapy I told him to relinquish everything and "take to the hills":

"Go barefooted, get some ragged clothes, buy a skillet, find a shack, and live in the mountains."

I specified a place where I knew he could go and lead a completely hillbilly life, with no ambitions of any sort. How did he fare? I've forgotten his exact words, but a very competent observer [who lived near my patient's shack] said: "He's fat and sassy. He can even eat his own cooking, and he must have a cast-iron stomach to eat his own cooking!"

His ulcers? Well, of course, they were psychogenic in origin. He is relaxed, and happy, and comfortable; and he is perfectly willing to spend another six months there, or longer. But in my view, he has settled for a mediocre goal. You know, I would like to have him do something more than just enjoy the physical life. I would like to have him plant a flower garden along that shack in which he is living. It is an unessential thing, but I would like him to make a lawn around that shack. I would like to have him pretty up the place—maybe build some nice rural furniture. But it's not essential.

This boy had never learned to do anything for *his* satisfaction; he only knew how to do things for the satisfaction of others. Yet he has been taught that you do a job well, and you do it for satisfaction. But give him an unessential job, and—well, *somebody's* got to be pleased with it. In that isolated place, there is only one person to be satisfied; *he himself* would have to furnish the satisfaction for that yard. But I'm afraid he isn't going to do it. I'm going to put a bug in his ear indirectly, to see if I can't get him to do an unessential task and learn, in that elementary fashion, the importance of *self*-satisfaction.

The Double Bind in Dentistry

Associating Denture Comfort with Behavioral Inevitabilities: A Two-Level Double Bind

[*Question from the audience concerns the application of the double bind in helping dental patients accept the wearing of dentures.*]
You can say:

"There are various ways of getting used to your dentures, and I don't know the most convenient time for you to sit down and give attention to the fitting feeling of the dentures in your mouth. I suppose a good time to study how nicely your jaws are accommodating your dentures would be right after a meal when you've been using them to enjoy your food, or just before you go to bed."

You really don't know what time it will be, but you tie it to the pleasantness of the meal, to the convenience of just before bedtime. Either way, you've committed them to the idea of discovering the comfortableness with which their *jaws* are accommodating the dentures. And if they don't study it as you've suggested, then what have they left? There is the discovery of the comfortableness of their *dentures* [on their jaws]. So you win all the way around. You've got a double bind within a double bind, and the patient can't see either of them. Even if he neglects, he is bound.

The Double Bind to Utilize Resistance and Facilitate Learning

Juxtaposing a Positive and a Negative to Set Personal Limits and Evoke Self-Motivation; Giving Students the "Choice" of Emotional Satisfaction

[*Question from the audience concerns the use of hypnosis and posthypnotic suggestion in facilitating learning and recall abilities in students.*]

You are proposing a question wherein you are treading upon another person's rights. The student has a right to learn in his own way. Therefore, whenever I am called upon to handle a child in this matter of learning, I do the following. I put the child in a trance, but as soon as the child is in a trance I state:

"Your parents want me to use hypnosis to help you learn more easily. But let's get things straight. *You* have to do the learning, and *you* have to like to do the learning. *I'm* not going to make you learn, and I'm not even going to make you like to learn. All I'm interested in is that *you do not learn one bit more than you want to learn.*"

Do you see the double bind there?

"I want you to be sure to see to it that you do not learn one bit more than you want to learn."

The child is bound to learn, and he is bound to learn clear up to the point of his limit. *I want you to be sure* is a very positive statement; *that you do not learn* meets his negative attitude; *one bit more* means he's got to recognize that he does have to learn, and that learning is part of life's experience; *not one bit more than you want to* is saying that the child does want to learn. And you say very emphatically:

"Not one bit more *than you want to.*"

This statement says that the child does want to learn, but then he is also told *not to learn one bit more,* which gives him the chance of refusing to learn. Yet he is also bound to accept learning because he does want to learn, but at the same time he can reject that one little bit more than he wants to learn. So when you try to teach a student to use hypnosis, or you use hypnosis to inspire him, you give him a double bind that permits him to be inspired *only by the drives within himself.*

With younger children I say:

"There is a lot of pleasure and satisfaction in your C's. Every mark has its meaning, and certainly a C is better than a D, and a D is better than a failure."

You're darn right that a D is better than a failure, and a C is better than a D; and you don't go on to emphasize that a B is better than a C, and an A is better than a B. If the student doesn't know that by now, you are wasting time talking about it.

"And I'd like to have you get all the pleasure that you want from your grades. If you are content with the emotional satisfaction of a D, please keep right on getting D's. But, remember, I said *if.* And if you want C's, for heaven's sake get the C, and get all the satisfaction you want from the C."

All I want the child to do is get emotional satisfaction from his grades.

210

PART VI

Expanding Human Potentials In Illness And Injury[1]

What's *Right* with Mind and Body

*The Therapeutic Reframing of Problems: Developing a
Positive Body Awareness as a Context for Enjoying Life
Despite Illness or Disability: "It's a **Good** Elbow!";
The Six-Acre Scar; Wearing Your
Wheelchair Like an Adornment*

In this matter of the interrelationships between hypnosis, physical illness, and human behavior, I can recall one very illustrative experience. My children and I were watching a carpenter who was doing some work for us out in the backyard. He hit his thumb with the hammer, and the limping he did was marvelous! He limped all around, hanging onto that painful thumb of his. Now why did he *limp* when he had hit himself on the *thumb*? Because *whenever we have any kind of injury, we alter our concept of ourselves.*

The question was raised, How do you help a patient with a scar? When my seven-year-old son collided with a truck, the plastic surgeon looked him over and remarked very truthfully, "When he is close-up, his girlfriends will think the scar is cute. So let's not do anything to it."[2] It is important to be able to look at things that way.

When people get sick, you see the best and the worst of

211

their being. You ought to appreciate that, and you ought to give them permission to feel that they have the right to misbehave. But you can always ask them, "Do you have to misbehave that amount?" My daughter Christine had a cut on her leg, and she didn't like it because it was going to leave a scar. She was making a great big fuss about it. But she also wasn't going to tell her boyfriend that it was healing all right, because she got more attention from him complaining about it! He was in another state going to the university. It was a nice area to discuss, a nice way to maintain relations.

People like to talk about their illnesses, their hurts, their pains, everything that is wrong with them. But you also ought to be aware that they can talk to you about how *good* they feel. You need to encourage them to be interested in knowing that even though they do have a painful area of the body, *it is so nice that all the rest of the body is all right.* You need to teach people the importance of knowing that their body is a good one.

I can think of the time that Christine was visiting a friend when she was 10 years old. Her mother and I were in Chicago at a meeting. Christine fell and broke her elbow. The general practitioner to whom she was taken examined her, put on a cast, and then told her she shouldn't worry—the elbow would heal just fine and without a scar. She responded as a conceited 10-year-old, "Of course, it will heal. It's a good elbow!" He talked to me on the phone afterwards, and he said that it was a very nice experience to treat a child who knew that she had a good elbow.

Everyone should have that awareness about themselves. Why should anybody ever think adversely about their body? If they have an appendix that is inflamed, be glad! They can be very proud that it is greatly inflamed, because it means that the rest of their body is going to take care of that inflammation. That particular disability is an interesting one. It can be something that is pleasing to them because it is also passing—here today but gone tomorrow.

Why should any person take this year's failure in a high school course or a college course seriously? This semester is here today but tomorrow it will be gone. I think that you need to convey that attitude to a person in every possible situation. You talk to a patient who has recently become blind and what should you tell him? Not about the handicaps of being blind—he will discover those all by himself. You won't need to tell him anything along those lines. But you can tell him that he is going to discover an increased ability to hear, an increased ability to taste, an increased ability to become aware of changes around him—and the changes and the abilities are all completely fascinating.

So many people look on patients as suffering from arthritis [as if that were the only thing to notice]. It is true, they do have arthritis. But they also have a lot more to them than the arthritis. That is the thing that patients tend to forget: that they have more to them than arthritis, and that they ought to be very, very much aware that there is something more than arthritis in their lives. In fact, you know, arthritis really isn't important at all. It's annoying, it's a nuisance, but the important thing is that they can do so many other things that are important.

The girl with the very large nose—how important is that? Has she ever realized that she has a cupid's bow on the upper lip? That her lower lip invites kisses? What chap is going to look at that large nose when he really wants to kiss her?[3]

I can recall a college student who had been in an automobile accident when she was much younger. She had a scar that was six acres in size along the right side of her mouth. I had her draw a sketch of it while looking in the mirror, and she used a full sheet of paper to draw it. It was star-shaped. I told her that if she dated a boy, she would discover that the boy would always want to kiss her on the scar side of her mouth. She didn't believe me, but she tried it out and discovered I was right!

Why did her boyfriends kiss her on that side of her mouth? Because she always tipped her head in that direction. I wasn't making a mistake, because I knew what she would do. She would wonder whether they would kiss her on that side of her mouth, she would unconsciously tip that side of her head up, and they would oblige her! In fact, she found out that every young man she dated liked that scar, and she asked me questions about this matter of why she ever thought the scar was so very large?[4]

People take the attitude that their illnesses are so important. You need to recognize the attitude that patients have toward their own illnesses. *[After recounting a few examples already familiar to our readers, Erickson talks about his attitude toward his own polio that left him in a wheelchair for the last 30 years of his life.]* You can give people the feeling that you are not physically handicapped. *You just wear the wheelchair as an adornment.* I don't think the wheelchair is all that important. It is what I have to say, what I have to talk about, that is important. In dealing with medical, surgical, and dental patients, you need to recognize what is wrong with them physically, and then recognize that they need to be told *what is right with them physically and psychologically.*

Reframing Hips and Hiccups

Irrational Association of Words and Symptoms?; Converting Negative into Positive via Truisms Evoking a Yes Set; Shock, Surprise, and Personal Truth; Reframing Wide Hips; Depotentiating Resistance by Letting the Patient Take Credit for the Cure; Indirect Posthypnotic Suggestion with "Psychobiological Facilitation"

I can recall a young woman who had a very broad pelvis. She never met anybody in the hospital corridor without making a vicious swing of her hips at them—be they male or female. She developed hiccups and hiccuped for about three weeks. She was very resentful when she was told that I ought to be called in to see her, but she finally couldn't stand it anymore. I walked in and with my usual tact said:

"You don't want to see me, but you will be interested in certain ideas that I would like to tell you about. I've seen your great big fanny, but every time you see visitors come with small children, there is an awfully soft light in your eyes. You really would like to become a mother. Have you ever read the *Song of Solomon?* What kind of a man do you think you would like to marry? Do you think you'd like to marry a man who looked at that wide pelvis of yours as a cradle for children? I think that is the kind of a man you would like to marry. All the use you will ever make of your hips is to sit on them. But the man who marries you can look upon your pelvis breadth as a cradle for children."

Her attitude changed completely. I agreed with her that she should not give me any credit for the change in her hiccups. It was 4 o'clock in the afternoon and she would continue to hiccup after I left. But somewhere around 11 or 11:30 that evening, the hiccups would spontaneously disappear and nobody would attribute their disappearance to me. But she could enjoy the fact that some man looking at her would really want to marry her.

Sometime later she brought a young man into the office and showed me her engagement ring. They talked about the house they were going to have, and the nursery, and the number of children *he* wanted. But she and I knew that she wanted children, too.

Rossi: Erickson recounted this case to me on a number of occasions to illustrate the various facets that he thought were involved in its successful outcome. First, we can only speculate that the words *hips* and *hiccups* are harmonically related in a way that could account for their symptomatic association. So tenuous is this *irrational association,* however, that I will say no more about it.

Erickson's first phrase to her, "You don't want to see me," uses a variety of indirect hypnotic forms.[5] First of all, it is the absolute truth about the initial *resistance* she is experiencing. Since it is the truth, she can only respond to it with an internal acknowledgment of *yes.* Thus, her initial attitude of *no* was immediately converted into an affirmative one. This *yes* is then reinforced with an appealing second phrase, "you will be interested in certain ideas that I would like to tell you about." Her initial resistance is thus depotentiated and she is now open to receiving "interesting ideas."

The second sentence is a classical Ericksonian use of shock and surprise to open up a recognition of the truth of personal experience. The initial phrase, "I've seen your great big fanny," has got to be a surprising shock, and it would normally arouse the most violent resistance. But Erickson immediately uses this shock to open up the surprising truth of his intimate understanding of her in his next statement: " . . . with small children there is an awfully soft light in your eyes. You really would like to become a mother." In these first three sentences, Erickson has thus come to the heart of the matter.

He then follows this up with three fascinating questions about the *Song of Solomon* (religious appeal?), the kind of man who would like to marry her (an interesting reversal of her probably more narcissistic preoccupation of what kind of a man *she* would like to marry), and, finally, the really important suggestive association between this man and her hips: ". . . you'd like to marry a man who looked at that wide pelvis of yours as a cradle for children." What a beautiful reframe! Wide hips that she defiantly thrust at the world as an apparent act of aggression are softly reframed as "a cradle for children" that will be the essence of her appeal as a woman for the right man.

Who was it that said there is no limit to what one can accomplish if one let's others have credit for it? Erickson uses this idea to depotentiate any lingering resistance by ensuring that she will not have to let him take the credit for her hiccup cure, since it will not take place until later that night.

This is actually an indirect posthypnotic suggestion with what I call "psychobiological facilitation."[6] The suggestion is biologically facilitated by the fact that it is given at "breaking point": that important psychobiological shift that takes place at mid-afternoon when our mind-body shifts from the upward arc of being awake in the daytime, downward to the nighttime arc in preparation for sleep.[7] This is also one of the two periods of the day (11 A.M. and 4 or 5 P.M.) when hypnotizability is greatest.[8]

Depotentiating Fear in Terminal Illness

Metaphorical and Fantasized Use of "Splinting" to Reinforce Muscles for Walking; Learning to Enjoy "Every Solitary Thing in Life"

You look comprehensively at patients, whether they are well, whether they are ill, and you try to get an understanding of each personality. You do not let patients get frightened by a mere cancer. Why should they? I can think of Cathy, who had been told that she had one month to live. I told Cathy:

"That's one doctor's guess. Another doctor's guess would be two, and mine would be different. Who gives a darn about the whole length of a guess? What I would like to have you do is to discover that you have got enough time to enjoy fully all the things you really want to enjoy. You will give that time to those things. You won't put off your enjoyment. You will really enjoy every thing you want to enjoy."

I called her physician and asked about the advisability of Cathy walking. He said that she might suffer fractures if she got out of bed. So I went in to Cathy and told her:

"You've got some muscles in your legs, muscles in your hips, and why not use them? You know that people with broken bones automatically contract their muscles and splint the broken bone, so before you get off this bed, enjoy splinting the muscles of your thighs, the muscles of your hips, and walk to the living room, the dining room, the kitchen, the playroom of your three boys. You will enjoy seeing that playroom, since you are a mother, 36 years old, and you will really enjoy knowing what the playroom of a seven-, nine- and 11-year old boy really looks like. You will enjoy noticing the disorder that your husband has created in the kitchen, but you will also know that the boys have enjoyed eating. Walk through all those rooms, your thighs nicely splinted, your hips nicely splinted. You can even go to the bathroom. That, too, is a pleasure. You might even walk through those rooms twice just in case you missed any pleasures."

Cathy did walk through twice just in case she had missed any pleasures. Then she got back in her bed and she started to enjoy every solitary thing in life. I don't know how many things she enjoyed, because just how many things are there in one's memory that one can enjoy?

Increasing Awareness of Potentials via Hypnosis

Restricting Illness, Expanding Joy and Potentials: Erickson's Father's Happy Death at 97: "Still More Coronaries to Go"

I can think of a time when I broke two toes and how I limped. It really wasn't important the next day. I was able to do everything in spite of a very small pain in my foot. It wasn't worthwhile seeing a general practitioner. It is the way you look at the self; the way you discover that you have an illness, an injury, and you abide by the restrictions. *But you are also delighted that you have all these other parts of you with which to enjoy life.*

I think my father was a plague to his doctor and his

surgeon. His doctor tried to tell my sister, "Your father is in his early 80s, he is unconscious from that coronary, and his chances of living are not very good. My sister's response was, "You just don't know my father."

When my father recovered consciousness he said, "A week's time wasted lying here in the hospital!" When he had his second coronary in his mid-80s, the same doctor was present when my father again recovered consciousness. My father said, "Another week wasted!"

He also had an obstruction of the bowel that required the removal of nine feet of intestine. When he came out of the anesthetic he said, "I'll be 10 days instead of a week's time."

He had his third coronary in his late 80s. When he recovered consciousness he told the physician, "Well, there are still more coronaries to go." Why not? When he had his fourth coronary in his early 90s he said: "Really, doctor, I thought that one would carry me off. I'm beginning to lose faith in the fifth. All I hope for is that when I die, I will be very happy." He was well past his 97th birthday when he had a massive cerebral hemorrhage. Well, he should have lost faith in that fifth coronary! There had to be something more than a coronary.

I can think of my brother-in-law who said, "Look at those two fools running up that hill," referring to my father and mother. They were in their 80s and he was just past 60. My parents didn't know that they weren't supposed to be able to run uphill in their 80s. They were excited to visit the home they had lived in 50 years ago in the Rocky Mountains of Nevada, and they just naturally ran up the hill!

Illness is part of life's experience. You restrict it by focusing on such-and-such joys, that's all. But what about all the rest of your life experiences? When you are using hypnosis with your patients, as soon as you start impressing upon them the tremendous importance of the enjoyment of all the other things they possess, a great wealth of other things, then they can listen to you. You can use hypnosis not just to induce relief of pain from arthritis, relief of pain from a burn, but *you can use hypnosis to make the patient aware of other potentialities.* You don't have to go to any great extent in doing that.

It's All in How You Look at It!

*Depotentiating an Inferiority Complex by Centering
Attention on the "Really Important Things"; Reframing
Stuttering as the Early Stages of Learning to Speak;
Correcting Stuttering by Learning the Pleasure of
Making Infantile Sounds*

A girl comes into your office with a great big inferiority complex, and she doesn't think she deserves to be in your office. She doesn't think she ought to speak to you, that she doesn't deserve any attention whatsoever, probably doesn't know that she has eyes of blue, a very beautiful blue. She doesn't know, perhaps, that she has the widow's peak, that she has a very nice arch to her eyebrows. While you are centering her attention on those really important things, you take care of the inferiority complex.[9]

Take a stutterer who really knows how to stutter. He stutters as well as any newborn baby who says, *"goo-goo, goo-goo, goo-goo,"* endlessly. That is the baby who is going to learn to talk, you know. He can say *da, da, da, da* in completely meaningless ways, but he is going to learn to talk. I think that is the important point that should be emphasized when working with a patient who stutters. You do not emphasize the fact that he thinks he has poor communication with other people. He doesn't have poor communication—he merely *thinks* that. You give him a totally different feel on the subject of his stuttering.

I told one stutterer who used a paper pad to communicate (he was a senior in college and had gone through college with that pad!):

"You know that you can learn to write in the third grade. What most people don't know is that you learn to talk when you are very young. And you tell me that you've only got three hours in which to see me before you return to Los Angeles. Well, suppose you go to Los Angeles for the summer and see

220

how many infantile sounds you can make, and how you can *enjoy* making them. Because that is the way every good speaker learns how to talk. Then at the end of the summer, before you go back to your university, drop in to see me. You might possibly want to see me again, maybe just to exchange words with me. In all events, there ought to be something to talk about by next August or next September."

At the end of the summer he walked into the office and said, "I'm afraid I've cheated you out of a lot of fees, Doctor, because I've been *goo-gooing* all summer long, and it was a very pleasant experience. I seemed to recall childhood memories of putting together *goo's* and *ma's* and *da's*, and yet I paid you for only three hours. Don't you think I really ought to see you for several hours and pay you for them just to visit with you?"

What happened to the stuttering? Neither he nor I cared. What we cared about was that he really enjoyed making noises like a small infant, and that he learned to add two sounds together, and three sounds together in a meaningful way. And he didn't look upon this correction of his speech as a *correction of his speech* but as a *learning*. And that is a very important difference.[10]

When you use hypnosis, you ask a person to enjoy being himself by your manner, by your tone of voice, by your general attitude in every way, and *you make the enjoyment of being the self a most important thing*, because it is important to the individual.

Utilizing Handicaps to Expand Potentials

Erickson's Wealth of Learnings from His Wheelchair;
Modern Neurological Support for Erickson's Perspective

What can patients do with their particular illnesses? Are patients as handicapped as others think they are? They are not.

Everybody thinks that illness constitutes a handicap, but does it really? *You want patients to recognize that illness, physical disability, is merely one part of their total life experience—* and I am speaking as one who really knows! You haven't any idea of all the things I've learned about life since I got that wheelchair. It is completely amazing! That wheelchair has taught me an awful lot about the value of life, of living, and the important things that you can have. It really isn't a handicap.

In fact, I can feel sorry for some of you who have to use your legs and your feet to do things like climb stairs. I listen to my two teenage daughters talking about the 486 steps they climbed up the Washington Monument and the 486 steps they climbed down—and they felt every one of those steps! I know I could look at the Washington Monument without climbing a single step. I can see it thoroughly.

I would also agree that if I didn't have the wheelchair, I would enjoy every bit of the fatigue, every bit of the tiredness of walking up and down those 486 steps. People are entitled to feel tired. They are entitled to look upon illness, fatigue, pain, distress of any sort as part of the meaningfulness of life itself. They ought not to view it as something to be afraid of. Why should patients be frightened by some kind of illness or disability? They have so much else to enjoy. When you use hypnosis, you include those kinds of ideas in your technique so that patients can understand that they brought into your office a lot more than an appendix, an ulcer, a cancer, an arthritic joint.

I know a man who is blind, whom I've visited on a number of occasions. He is a masseur, and you can't imagine the way he uses his fingers to "see" a patient. I asked him to do a massage on one of my patients and his feedback to me was: "That woman is awfully tense, awfully concerned about herself. But she won't be when I finish with her. She is a rather remarkably beautiful woman and she knows it. She really knows that she is unique—the only one of her kind in the history of humankind!" My blind friend could feel all that with his fingers as he worked on this woman's legs. How did she convey that message to him through a massage he was giving her legs? But she did convey it, and so should you convey to your patients an awareness of all the other things they possess.

Rossi: Erickson's way of helping patients utilize their so-called handicaps to expand their potentialities has now become a basic principle in humanistic and transpersonal psychology. In his recent book, *Peace, Love, and Healing,* Bernie Siegel expands this attitude to enhance healing in traditional medicine, citing Erickson's work as a reference point.

The factual basis of Erickson's approach can be found in modern neurology, where it is now documented that when sensory input from a normal organ or limb is restricted by a handicap (blindness or amputation of a limb, for example), the cellular brain fields that were devoted to the handicapped part are now taken over by another part of the body. This can result in the enhancement of the sensory-perceptual and motor coordination potentialities of the part of the body that takes over the brain field.[11] This may account, in part, for the compensatory enhancement of certain skills and the development of new potentials in those who are physically challenged.

PART VII

Creative Choice In Therapeutic Hypnosis

CONTINUING THE LEGACY OF GREGORY BATESON AND MILTON H. ERICKSON

Ernest L. Rossi
and
Patrick A. Jichaku

In their epoch-making paper, "Toward a Theory of Schizophrenia," which introduced the concept of the double bind, Gregory Bateson and his co-workers noted four points that are relevant to this volume:

1) the role of hypnosis in their original formulation of the concept of the double bind;

2) the therapeutic implications of the double bind;

3) its relation to the Zen koan; and

4) a multitude of culturally interesting behaviors (play, humor, poetry, drama, fiction, ritual, and creative processes in general) that all had *self-reference* as their common denominator. They described their views as follows (Bateson, Jackson, Haley, & Weakland, 1956):

We are giving extensive attention to hypnosis. A

225

great array of phenomena that occur as schizophrenic symptoms—hallucinations, delusions, alterations of personality, amnesias, and so on—can be produced temporarily in normal subjects with hypnosis. These need not be directly suggested as specific phenomena, but can be the "spontaneous" result of an arranged communication sequence. For example, Erickson (1955) will produce a hallucination by first inducing catalepsy in a subject's hand and then saying, "There is no conceivable way in which your hand can move, yet when I give the signal, it must move." That is, he tells the subject his hand will remain in place, yet it will move, and in no way the subject can consciously conceive. When Erickson gives the signal, the subject hallucinates the hand moved, or hallucinates himself in a different place and therefore the hand was moved. This use of hallucination to resolve a problem posed by contradictory commands which cannot be discussed seems to us to illustrate the solution of a double bind situation via a shift in logical types. Hypnotic responses to direct suggestions or statements also commonly involve shifts in type, as in accepting the words, "Here's a glass of water" or "You feel tired" as external or internal reality, or in literal response to metaphorical statements, much like schizophrenics. We hope that further study of hypnotic induction, phenomena, and waking will, in this controllable situation, help sharpen our view of the essential communicational sequences which produce phenomena like those of schizophrenia.

. . . . The understanding of the double bind and its communicative aspects may lead to innovations in therapeutic techniques. Just what these innovations may be is difficult to say, but on the basis of our investigations we are assuming that double bind situations occur consistently in psychotherapy. At times these are inadvertent in the sense that the therapist is imposing a double bind situation similar to that in the patient's history, or the patient is imposing a double bind situation on the therapist. At other times therapists seem to impose double binds, either deliberately or intuitively, which force the patient to respond differently than he had in the past. (pp. 20-21)

For the purposes of this section, we may say that the pertinent characteristics of double binds always involve the following:

1) messages on at least two or more levels;
2) a paradoxical conflict between these messages;
3) messages which comment on themselves (self-referential metastatements);
4) messages involving personal issues that are highly motivating;
5) a subjective experience of puzzlement, confusion, and a curiously binding sense of absorption or entrancement as the subject recursively reviews the paradoxical messages in an attempt to clarify and resolve them.

The first three characteristics are all well documented features of the *logical double bind*. The last two characteristics, however, are *psychological phenomena* that are evoked when the paradoxical aspects of the double bind interact with human experience. These logical and psychological characteristics of the double bind are intermixed in the current literature (Berger, 1978; Sluzki & Ransom, 1976) to the point where it is extremely difficult to differentiate between them. Therefore, the first purpose of this section is to clearly differentiate between logical and psychological double binds.

The Logical Double Bind: A Simplified Format

Since presentations about logical double binds are invariably difficult to grasp, we will introduce a simplified format to outline them. Later, this new format will enable us to distinguish among the varieties of hypnotic double binds and will provide us with a practical method for generating new therapeutic double binds. We will begin by illustrating the logical double bind in three steps depicted in Figures 1 through 3.

Figure 1 illustrates the basic situation in which a statement in italics comments on the truth value of another statement framed in a box below. The italicized statement is more abstract (or secondary) because it comments on the primary-level statement in the frame below it. In this section, a *statement about a statement* is called a *metastatement* and will always be italicized. In Figure 1 there is no problem with paradox or double binds, because the metastatement and the primary-level statement are placed on different levels, as they should be for logical clarity.

In the language of mathematics and logic developed by Whitehead and Russell (1910), the metastatement and the primary-level statement are said to be of different logical types. Since the metastatement is a different logical type, it is placed above and *outside* the frame that contains the primary-level statement, "I love you." There is no ambiguity in Figure 1. The statement within the frame, "I love you," is labeled as false by the metastatement commenting on it. Therefore we can logically conclude that the total situation in Figure 1 means, "I don't love you."

In Figure 2 we have a dramatically different situation. The metastatement in italics has been placed within the same frame as the primary-level statement. This means that the metastatement comments *on itself* as well as on the primary-level statement

All statements within this frame are false.

> "I love you."

Figure 1: The metastatement in italics is of a different logical type and on a more abstract level than the primary-level statement within the box (frame). Since these two statements are clearly illustrated to be on different levels, there is no confusion between them.

beneath it. Because the metastatement comments on itself, it has become *self-referential*. Because it comments in a nega-tive fashion about its own truth value, it becomes *paradoxical*.

Figure 2 illustrates the famous Epimenides paradox: If it is true, then it is false; if it is false, then it is true. Logicians take great care to avoid the situation depicted in Figure 2 precisely because it generates paradoxical and illogical conclusions. In essence, it wrecks the structure of an otherwise satisfactory, logical pattern. Since the paradoxical metastatement in Figure 2 comments on the truth value of the primary-level statement, "I love you," then it, in turn, becomes ambiguous. Since the metastatement itself can be true or false, then the primary statement in the same frame of reference can be either true or false. Thus we have paradox and ambiguity, but not necessarily a double bind.

All statements within this frame are false.

"I love you."

Figure 2:   The metastatement is placed within the frame that it is commenting on and thus becomes self-referential and paradoxical. It thereby also corrupts the primary statement, "I love you," into ambiguity.

The double bind becomes fully established in Figure 3 in which we have added another statement on the primary level, "I hate you." Figure 3 contains three essential characteristics of the logical double bind that are important to note:

1) *There is a self-referential metastatement* that generates paradox because it comments negatively on its own truth value.
2) *There are contradictory primary-level statements.*
3) *There is a recursive cycle of shifting truth valus* generated by the inclusion of the meta- and primary-level statements within the same frame of reference.

These three characteristics of the logical double bind are forbidden operations in the theory of logical types (Whitehead & Russell, 1910). This bane of the logician, however, provides opportunity for the psychologist, as we now explore the psychological aspects of this double bind in Figure 3.

All statements within this frame are false.

"I love you."
"I hate you."

Figure 3: This illustrates a fully developed logical double bind. The self-referential metastatement sets up a recursive cycle between the shifting truth values of the two primary statements, "I love you" and "I hate you," that are themselves mutually self-contradictory. (Modified from Bateson, 1972/1988)

The Psychological Double Bind as a Phenomenon of Self-Reference, Entrancement, and Creativity

If you, the reader, really puzzle over the paradoxical process of working through the shifting meanings of the messages on different levels of the double bind in Figure 3, you will notice the experience of concentrated attention and deep absorption or *entrancement* that is required. *Paradox and psychological double binds thus induce an experience akin to trance when they fully capture the subject's attention with a highly motivating issue.*

Bateson (1972/1988) has commented on the experience of the double bind as follows: " 'I,' however, exist in the communicational world as an essential element in the syntax of my experience and in the experience of others, and the communications of others may damage my identity, even to the point of breaking up the organization of my experience" (p. 251). A speculative generalization of this section would be that it is precisely this "breaking up [of] the organization of my experience" that can lead to illness as well as growth and creativity. While the *pathologic double bind* leads to the personality deterioration of schizophrenia and neurosis, the *therapeutic double bind* can facilitate the breaking up of old frames of reference as a preliminary step so that new patterns

230

of understanding can become manifest through personality growth and maturation. We would generalize further that this breaking up of old frames of reference is a necessary preliminary to the emergence of new patterns of understanding in art and science. The subjective sense of significance in such apparently diverse experiences as humor, play, drama, poetry, ritual, hypnosis and creative moments (Rossi, 1972/1985, 1973) in art and science may all be patterns of highly recursive neurological activity sorting through the implications of the multilevel self-referential messages of the psychological double bind. A recursive experience of absorption that merely leads to the breakdown of an older, more limited and problematic frame of reference but leaves one in puzzlement and dissatisfaction could lead to depression or a variety of other syndromes (Sluzki & Vernon, 1976). However, when a subject is able to contain this breakdown phase with equanimity and successfully incubate for a time to permit a restructuring of life experience into broader frames of reference, then creative moments of new insight can be experienced with positive affect (Rossi, 1972/1985).

We are currently engaged in studies exploring this role of the psychological double bind and entrancing experience in the creative processes of the arts and sciences. For the purposes of this section, however, we will focus only on three forms of the psychological double bind that are currently emerging on different levels of hypnotherapeutic practice.

Three Forms of the Psychological Double Bind

The independent efforts of Haley, Cheek, and Rossi have described how the double bind operates on different levels of the hypnotherapeutic process, ranging from the interpersonal to the psychophysiological. As we shall see, however, they have not yet made the distinction between the logical and psychological double bind that we are clarifying in this paper and, indeed, did not always know when they were generating double binds. In most of their work the discovery of the operation of a double bind was usually a *post hoc* realization.

1. *Haley's Interpersonal Double Bind as a Model for Strategic Family Therapy*

At Bateson's suggestion in the early 1950s, Haley and Weakland studied the hypnotic work of Milton H. Erickson and discovered that he was, indeed, using what the Bateson group termed the *double bind* (Erickson, Haley, & Weakland, 1959; Haley, 1976). As originally conceived by the Bateson group, the double bind was an aspect of communication theory which was studied as an *interpersonal process,* particularly between family members. Thus when Haley later formulated his chapter, "How Hypnotist and Subject Maneuver Each Other" (1976), he focused on how the double bind was used in an interpersonal, authoritarian context where the hypnotist used "challenges" as a criterion of his genuine hypnotic control over the subject's behavior. Haley described this model as follows:

> Although the imposition of paradoxical directive is implicit in every hypnotic induction, in some situations it is more obvious than in others. For example, during a lecture on hypnosis a young man said to Milton H. Erickson, "You may be able to hypnotize other people, but you can't hypnotize me!" Dr. Erickson invited the subject to the demonstration platform, asked him to sit down, and then said to him, "I want you to stay awake, wider and wider awake, wider and wider awake." The subject was faced with a double level message: "Come up here and go into a trance," and "Stay awake." *He knew that if he followed Erickson's suggestions, he would go into a trance.* [This is the hidden paradoxical implication.] Therefore he was determined not to follow his suggestions. Yet if he refused to follow the suggestions to stay awake, he would go into a trance. Thus he was caught in a paradox. Note that these were not merely two contradictory messages; they were two levels of messages. The statement "Stay awake" was qualified by, or framed by, the message "Come up here and go

into a trance." Since one message was qualified by another, they were of different levels of message. Such conflicting levels of message may occur when verbal statement, tone of voice, body movement, or the contextual situation qualify each other incongruently. A double level message may occur in a single statement. For example, if one person says to another, "Disobey me," the other person is faced with an incongruent set of directives and can neither obey nor disobey. *If he obeys, he is disobeying, and if he disobeys, he is obeying.* The statement "Disobey me" contains a qualification of itself and can be translated into "Don't obey my commands," and the simultaneous qualifying statement, "Don't obey my command to not obey my commands." A hypnotic challenge consists of this type of request. (p. 35) [Italics added]

Figure 4 illustrates Haley's first example of Erickson's double-binding hypnotic induction. The metalevel suggestion in italics is a hidden *unverbalized implication* that frames the two, contradictory, primary-level statements into a double bind.

If he followed Erickson's suggestions [in this frame], he would go into trance.

"Come up here and go into trance."
"Stay awake!"

Figure 4: An implied and unverbalized metalevel suggestion (in italics) frames the two, contradictory, primary-level statements into a double-binding hypnotic induction.

Figure 5 frames Haley's examples of how single statements can be double-binding, particularly in a hypnotic context where they are the prototype of "challenges." The metastatement in italics is once again an unverbalized implication that this is a hypnotic situation, context, or frame.

Haley's words follow Bateson's predominantly *logical* model of the double bind when he formulates the situation with "If he obeys, he is disobeying, and if he disobeys, he is obeying." This is still the language of the logician attempting to explain the Epimenides paradox.

Every statement in this frame is a trance-inducing challenge.

"Stay awake!"
"Disobey me!"

Figure 5: Another unverbalized metalevel suggestion (in italics) defining the context as hypnotic, so that each primary-level suggestion is framed into a double-binding "challenge" that generates "involuntary" responses.

Metastatements in Figures 4 and 5 are essentially different from those of Figures 2 and 3. The metastatement in Figures 2 and 3, "All statements within this frame are false," becomes a self-referential logical paradox when placed within a frame; it is a classical example of Epimenides' paradox. The metastatements in Figures 4 and 5 are also self-referential when placed within the frame, but they are not self-contradictory and do not necessarily generate an Epimenides paradox. From whence, then, comes their power to frame the primary level statements into double binds?

In Figures 4 and 5 the metastatements that frame the primary-level statements into double binds are *unverbalized implications*. As such, they are examples of what Erickson and Rossi (Erickson, Rossi & Rossi, 1976) have described as "psychological implication":

An understanding of how Erickson uses implication will provide us with the clearest model of his indirect approach to hypnotic suggestion. Since his use of "implication" may involve something more than the typical dictionary definition of the term, we will assume that he may be developing a special form of "psychological implication" in his work. For Erickson, psychological implication is a key that automatically turns the tumblers of a patient's associative processes into predictable patterns without awareness of how it happened. The implied thought or response seems to come up autonomously within patients, as if it were their own inner response rather than a suggestion initiated by the therapist. Psychological implication is thus a way of structuring and directing patients' associative processes when they cannot do it for themselves. The therapeutic use of this approach is obvious. If patients have problems because of the limitations of their ability to utilize their own resources, then implications are a way of bypassing these limitations. (pp. 59-60)

This concept of psychological implication can be used in the process of further clarifying the difference between logical and psychological double binds.

In the field of logic, self-referential metastatements that comment negatively on their own truth value are the basic mechanism for framing paradoxical and/or double-binding arguments. In the field of psychology, self-referential metastatements that contain psychological implications are the basic mechanism for framing paradoxical and/or double-binding experiences.

It is apparent from this distinction that Haley's early formulation of the double-bind approach to hypnotic suggestion is a bridge between the logical and the psychological. Haley uses the same logical language approach that Bateson uses in Figure 3, but Haley's double binds in Figures 4 and 5 utilize *psychological implication* as the essence of their metastatements rather than a logical paradox that comments negatively on its own truth value.

In Figure 6 we have outlined the earlier quoted example by Bateson of how Erickson double-binded a subject to hallucinate movement in a cataleptic hand. We find that it is an example of psychological double bind because its metalevel statement (in italics) is a psychological implication. This is in sharp contrast to the logical double bind of Figure 3 in which a metalevel statement comments negatively on its own truth value.

> *Erickson's suggestions are true and facilitate all sorts of unusual (hypnotic) behavior.*
>
> "There is no conceivable way in which your hand can move, yet when I give the signal, it must move."

Figure 6: Bateson's example of how Erickson facilitated the visual hallucination of a cataleptic hand moving. It is a psychological double bind because the hypothesized metastatement is an unverbalized psychological implication.

Indeed, we cannot find any published clinical examples of the use of the double bind in hypnosis that do not involve psychological implication. This leads us to conclude that in the field of hypnosis we are dealing with psychological double binds having highly motivating implications at the metalevel rather than with the purely logical double binds of the Epimenides type illustrated by Bateson in Figure 3.

Haley, like other role theorists, analyzes the hypnotic interaction on the interpersonal level as a highly directive and essentially manipulative process. This is the view of hypnosis as a process of influence communication wherein there is a power-play for the one-up position in which the therapist plays the role of an authoritative expert. This highly directive and authoritative role of the hynotherapist leads naturally to the branch of Erickson's work that contributes to the Brief Strategic Therapy currently in favor by those who use the systems theory approach to work with families (Haley, 1963, 1973, 1976, 1982; Watzlawick, 1982; Watzlawick, Weakland, & Fisch, 1974; Weakland, 1982).

2. *Cheek's Ideomotor Double Bind as a Model of Psychophysiological Hypnotic Responsiveness*

Simultaneously with Haley's work, a little heralded but profound shift was taking place in the way a new generation of clinicians was being trained in hypnosis in the 1950s and 1960s (Rossi & Cheek, 1988). This was the shift from the older, more authoritarian use of challenges as a criteria of trance to the new use of ideomotor signaling and indirect suggestion as permissive approaches better suited to clinical situations. LeCron published the first paper on ideomotor finger signaling (1954). However, apparently he had learned the use of ideomotor techniques from Erickson, who had developed them in the 1920s as an easier alternative to automatic writing (Cheek, 1961, 1984; Erickson, 1961/1980).

As a physician, surgeon, and obstetrician, Cheek has reported on his explorations of the psychophysiological application of ideomotor signaling techniques in publications over the past 23 years. In one report (1974) he outlines a triad of behavioral responses that accompanies the valid application of ideomotor signaling, particularly in recovering traumatic memories:

> From the author's exploration of surgical anesthesia memories, it has been apparent since 1957 that memory recall of deeply repressed information follows a natural sequence. The first indication that something meaningful is being recalled comes from the very deep zone of central nervous system reaction to a sensory stimulus involving physiological adaptations. Perspiration, increased respiratory and heart rate are the reflections before there is an ideomotor finger signal to show recognition of the stress. The more conscious horizon of thinking that can translate a feeling into speech is the last to get the message. This is a triad of greatest importance when it comes to trusting validity of final verbalization. (p. 265)

In a subsequent report (1975) Cheek continues:

> There are two benefits in having the subject repeatedly review the event at an ideomotor level of awareness

before attempting to obtain a verbal report. The first involves that apparent fact that each repetition at a deeper-than-verbal level of awareness accumulates more and more information as the stress of the experience is lessened. Repetition seems to raise the horizon of experience from the moment of its occurrence as a revivification to higher zones of thought that have developed later in life and therefore permit placing it into more distant perspective. The real event can be exposed to forces of conscious reason and reassessed. (p. 81)

When Cheek asks for a review of a traumatic memory or a dream, he orients the patient to the ideomotor signaling process with the direction, "Do not try to feel it consciously . . . First you must know the feelings subconsciously before you can feel them consciously" (Cheek, 1976, p. 24). To "know the feelings subconsciously" is actually a subtle form of the conscious/unconscious double bind (Erickson & Rossi, 1975/1980). Cheek is thus presenting the typically contradictory suggestions that double bind the patient into giving up the self-directing function of the ego to permit other, more involuntary levels of responsiveness to become manifest. Although Cheek never used the term *double bind* to describe this approach, it is evident from Figure 7 that his typical suggestions for ideomotor signaling (Cheek, 1976) fit the format of the psychological double bind.

All suggestions in this frame facilitate ideomotor signaling.

"Do not try to feel it consciously.
First you must know these feelings
subconsciously."

Figure 7: Cheek's ideomotor double bind evokes multilevel and recursive psychophysiological searches leading to a verbal response. The metalevel in italics is usually an unverbalized implication that carries a strong ideodynamic motivational force.

It is evident from the above figure that Cheek is using a double bind that intersects the physiological, the ideomotor, and the verbal levels. His ideomotor signaling approach evokes recursive inner searches on the "deeper" psychophysiological levels until the sought-for material reaches the verbal level. What is the nature of the psychophysiological levels that are being searched before the material reaches the verbal level?

At the present time we may hypothesize that the psychophysiological levels of information are encoded in the form of the neuro-hormonal and neuroendocrinal factors involved in memory storage and learning (McGaugh, 1983; Rosenzweig, 1984). Rossi would hypothesize further that memory traces of the specific patterning of ultradian cycles that accompany specific memories and learning could also serve as encoded information on the psychophysiological and ideomotor levels (Rossi, 1982, 1986a, 1991).

Because Cheek's ideomotor signaling approach "specializes" in the facilitation of recursive processes on the psychophysiological levels, it is most ideally suited for treatment of traumatic situations. Trauma can induce an altered state wherein memories are encoded in a statebound form that is frequently not available to ordinary ego consciousness. Cheek has classified these traumatic or altered-state situations as those of critical illness (1969), childbirth (1975, 1976), general anesthesia (1979), accidents, dream states (1965), and so forth. Cheek uses highly directive, short-term and exploratory efforts to quickly resolve symptoms and the effects of trauma that reach deeply into the psychophysiological levels of memory storage, imprinting, and learning. As such, Cheek's work (Rossi & Cheek, 1988) constitutes a pioneering effort to deal with what Erickson called the "neuro-psycho-physiological foundations of hypnosis" (1952/1980).

3. *Rossi's Exploratory Double Bind for Facilitating Intrapersonal Processes and Creative Choice*

Although every effort to provide an "objective record" of

Erickson's work was made by Rossi, it is becoming obvious in retrospect how his background as a humanistically-oriented clinical psychologist and Jungian analyst colored their collaborative publications (Erickson, Rossi, & Rossi, 1976; Erickson & Rossi, 1979, 1981). As a phenomenologically-oriented therapist, Rossi's questioning of Erickson elicited a set of commentaries that focused on the *intra*personal psychodynamic processes and mental mechanisms. Their collaboration also focused on the use of the "indirect forms of hypnotic suggestion" as the basic means of accessing an individual's potentials for facilitating a permissive, growth-oriented hypnotherapy. The double bind became a means of depotentiating the subject's "learned limitations" so that creative response possibilities ("lower" in the subject's response hierarchy) could be explored and facilitated into behavioral expression when appropriate. Their conceptualization of this constructive use of the "therapeutic" double bind in contrast to the destructive, schizophrenic double bind was expressed as follows (Erickson & Rossi, 1975/1980):

It may be noted in summary that the schizophrenic double bind carries negative injunctions that are enforced at the metalevel or abstract level that is outside the victim's control on the primary level. Erickson's therapeutic double binds, by contrast, always emphasize *positive agreement on the metalevel and offer alternatives that can be refused on the primary level.* Erickson has stated: "While I put patients into a double bind, they also sense, unconsciously, that I will never, never hold them to it. They know I will yield anytime. I will then put them in another double bind in some other situation to see if they can put it to constructive use because it meets their needs more adequately." For Erickson, then, the double bind is a useful device that offers a patient possibilities for constructive change. If one double bind does not fit, he will try another and another until he finds a key that fits ... *The structuring presence of a positive metalevel together with free choice on the primary level also defines the ethical use of the double bind.* (pp. 143-147)

Figure 8 outlines a typical form of the conscious-unconscious double bind that focuses on activating *intra*personal levels of creative problem resolution within the subject.

Your unconscious can have its own free choice of creative hypnotic response.

> "If your unconscious is ready to let you go into therapeutic trance to deal with that issue, you'll find yourself growing quiet with EYES CLOSING ALL BY THEMSELVES."

[If eyes do not close within 30 seconds, continue with:]

> "If the unconscious first needs to review another important issue, you'll find yourself DISCUSSING AN INTERESTING QUESTION that will prepare you for deeper trance work."

[If there is no apparent effort to speak within 30 seconds, continue with the third alternative:]

> "If you find yourself reluctant to speak, you can continue just as you are, allowing the unconscious to do what it needs to do, with your HEAD SLOWLY NODDING YES ALL BY ITSELF as you go deeper into trance."

Figure 8: An example of the Erickson-Rossi type of permissive induction with a psychological double bind containing a positive metalevel structuring a free creative choice among three therapeutic alternatives given on a primary level. Note how a behavioral marker (eyes closing, speaking, head nodding) is used to indicate which alternative is being accepted.

The Erickson-Rossi type of double bind is an example of the permissive, non-authoritarian, hypnotherapeutic approaches that facilitate creative choice in a manner that is more closely aligned with the humanistic, existential, and transpersonally oriented psychotherapies (Rossi & Cheek 1988). These permissive hypnotherapeutic approaches are ideally suited for facilitating personality development and for the creative, non-directive exploration of human potentials. The chart at the conclusion of this section provides an outline of the similarities and differences between the Haley, Cheek, and Rossi formulations of Erickson's work, and compares them with the Zen Buddhist use of koan as a form of "transpersonal double bind."

The Zen Koan as a Transpersonal Double Bind[1]

In their original paper on the double bind, Bateson and his co-workers (1956) used the following example of the Zen koan as a means of facilitating "Enlightenment" and contrasted it with the pathological situation of schizophrenia:

> In the Eastern religion, Zen Buddhism, the goal is to achieve Enlightenment. The Zen Master attempts to bring about enlightenment in his pupil in various ways. One of the things he does is to hold a stick over the pupil's head and say fiercely, "If you say this stick is real, I will strike you with it. If you say this stick is not real, I will strike you with it. If you don't say anything, I will strike you with it." We feel that the schizophrenic finds himself continually in the same situation as the pupil, but he achieves something like disorientation rather than enlightenment. The Zen pupil might reach up and take the stick away from the Master—who might accept this response—but the schizophrenic has no such choice since with him there is not caring about the relationship, and his mother's aims and awareness are not like the Master's. (pp. 7-8)

In figure 9 we have outlined the koan described in the above example to illustrate its structural similarity to the logical and psychological double binds.

> *Every understanding in this frame is false (unacceptable, unenlightened).*
>
> "This stick is real."
> "This stick is not real."

Figure 9: A self-referential metastatement defining a context of unenlightened responses or understandings.

To understand how the metastatement in Figure 9 is self-referential, we first need to recognize that Zen Enlightenment is an experience that transcends the dualistic forms of conceptual and rational knowledge—the dualities such as true/false, real/unreal, hot/cold, A/not A, and so forth. In the above koan the Zen Master not only negates both sides of the duality (real and not real), but in the process also negates his own metastatement—which is itself dualistic and must therefore be discarded.

Figure 9 illustrates that koans share at least structural characteristics of both the logical and psychological double binds. Like the logical double bind, the koan has a binding metastatement that negates itself as well as the two contradictory statements on the primary level. Like the psychological double bind, the binding metastatement in koans is frequently a psychological implication that is not as overtly expressed as in the example of Figure 9. In addition, koans also share functional characteristics with the logical and psychological double binds: if the aspirant is sincerely determined to become enlightened, koans can lead to the destruction of old, limited frames of reference so that new insights and enlightened experiences may emerge.

In Zen a koan is understood as both a *method* and an *expression:* It is a method which uses a paradoxical question or interaction to precipitate an enlightenment experience; it is an expression that is a straightforward presentation of what

Buddhists term "Thusness," or reality as-it-is. Because a psychological approach to the Zen koan has implications for understanding how the double bind facilitates personality transformations in hypnosis, we will discuss the koan here exclusively as a method. Koans and hypnotherapeutic double binds can then be related as means of catalyzing experiential insights by transcending the limitations of the "generalized reality orientation" (Shor, 1959) of the Western mind.

What are these limitations of the "generalized reality orientation" that can be transcended in the Zen koan? Typically they are "binds" whereby we become stuck in paradoxes, rigidities, and learned limitations caused by the dualistic preconceptions of our rational minds. These dualistic preconceptions are based on the logical process that places everything in a dualistic framework: either A or not A, right or wrong, 0 or 1 (in digital computers). Because individuals get stuck believing and behaving as if only one side of the duality could be correct, emotional and psychological rigidities become manifest. Those clinging to opposite sides of the duality come inevitably into futile conflict and war with one another (Hakuun, 1973). Neither side is right, since both are caught on the opposite side of the same duality. In the typical conflict, individuals are caught on opposing sides of the duality on the primary level. This is because they each accept the ensnaring metalevel implication that only one side can be right and that whoever capitulates, retreats, or compromises will lose their identity and become cowards. This is illustrated in Figure 10.

Only one way can be right, and you are cowards if you do not fight for your rights.

"This is my land," say People A.
"No, this is my land," say People B.

Figure 10: Two peoples bound in conflict on the primary level by a metastatement typical of the rational, dualistic mind that believes that only one side can be right.

The same process of conflict operates within individuals on the intrapersonal level, giving birth to inner conflicts, stress, and the consequent syndromes of psychopathology catalogued by psychiatry.

An important part of the process of Zen Enlightenment is a transcending or deconditioning of the limiting dualisms of the rational mind. In Western philosophy, Hegel referred to this process as the conflict between *thesis* and *antithesis* that had to be resolved through *synthesis* (Thilly & Wood, 1941). C. G. Jung based his "synthetic or constructive method" on transcending these dualistic polarities that limit the full integration and development of the personality (Jung, 1953, p. 80). In current day American psychology, this limitation of the rational mind is dealt with in humanistic and transpersonal psychology (Wilber, 1980, 1981) as the process of working through or extinguishing the conditioned patterns of perceptions, emotions, thinking, and behaving that limit our capacity for further growth. From this Western point of view koans can thus be conceptualized as *transpersonal double binds* that help people step out of *learned limitations,* which are those unfortunate patterns of conditioned response that block new learning by prematurely limiting and rigidifying one's skills and belief systems.

The method whereby the Zen Master or Roshi precipitates the experiential insight is metaphorically known as "cutting off the mind road" because the Roshi, during private interview with the student, negates or rebukes all dualistic and limited conceptual approaches to understanding the koan. The koan is used as a single point of contemplative focus; and single-mindedly, in response to the Roshi's instruction to become intimate or "one" with the koan, the aspirant absorbs himself into a recursive, subvocal inquiry or review of the koan.

After some period of such inquiry (it may be years), the moment finally arrives when the aspirant becomes so intimately absorbed, so concentrated in the koan, that the review of the koan becomes an autonomous and effortless action: the koan breathes the koan, as when, by comparative analogy, music may "play" the musician during periods of creative inspiration. In the midst of this condition or level of awareness, called *samadhi* in Zen, there is no consciousness of "I" as a personal construct. All dualistic rational distinctions between self and other, subjective and objective, inner and outer, are totally annihilated. There is only the koan which engages in everyday activities and experiences—the koan laughs and weeps, walks and rests, stands up and sits down.

During this condition—described in the literature as "pure like clear water, like a serene mountain lake, not moved by any wind" (Aitken, 1978)—the mind is ready and open for a spontaneous realization experience. At this point, any external or internal stimuli can catalyze an abrupt realization experience. It could be the sound of a temple bell, or the sight of peach blossoms in the distance, or an experience of physical pain.

It should be emphasized that falling into samadhi, or becoming deeply absorbed or entranced in the koan, is such an absolute prerequisite to becoming enlightened that no Enlightenment experience is ever possible without it. In fact, the depth and degree of the subsequent Enlightenment is positively correlated to the depth of the samadhi (Kasulis, 1981; Yamada, 1979). The Master Hakuin's story dramatically illustrates the importance of single-minded absorption and, subsequently, how any sudden or unexpected attention-fixating stimulus can precipitate Enlightenment. As the story is told, Hakuin was meditating on *Mu*, one of the most basic and popular Zen koans. In the Mu Koan, a monk asks Joshu in all earnestness, "Has a dog the Buddha nature or not?" Joshu said, "Mu" (translated as "No, does not have"). Hakuin (1686-1769) described his experience as follows (Yampolski, 1971):

> Night and day I did not sleep; I forgot both to eat and rest. Suddenly a great doubt [experience of absorption] manifested itself before me. It was as though I were frozen solid in the midst of an ice sheet extending tens of thousands of miles. A purity filled my breast and I could neither go forward nor retreat. To all intents and purposes I was out of my mind and *Mu* [koan] alone remained. Although I sat in the Lecture Hall and listened to the Master's lecture, it was as

though I were hearing a discussion from a distance outside the hall. At times it felt as though I was floating through the air.

This state lasted for several days. Then I chanced to hear the sound of the temple bell and I was suddenly transformed. It was as if a sheet of ice had been smashed or a jade tower had fallen with a crash. Suddenly I returned to my senses. I felt then that I had achieved the status of Yen-t'ou, who through the three periods of time encountered not the slightest loss (although he had been murdered by bandits). All my former doubts vanished as though ice had melted away. In a loud voice I called: "Wonderful, wonderful. There is no cycle of birth and death through which one must pass. There is no enlightenment one must seek. The seventeen-hundred koans handed down from the past have not the slightest value whatsoever." (p. 118)

We would suggest that while Hakuin's experience is of greater depth and completeness than that described by Bateson when he spoke of "breaking up the organization of my experience," both are describing aspects of the same process: breaking through limitations of an old mental framework into the liberation of experiencing something that transcends it.

The process of working through koans—of becoming deeply absorbed and of living through the impasses and frustration—is perhaps similar to what artists experience in the act of creating, and to what mathematicians and scientists endure in their efforts to resolve complex problems. All such processes involve a period of "being stuck" which is characterized by unconscious cerebration until new insights manifest themselves. We would submit that under the most ideal circumstances, the use of double binds in hypnotherapy can help patients break out of being "stuck" in problems.

How to Structure Therapeutic and/or Transpersonal Double Binds

We are now ready to outline a two-step operation that can be used to generate psychological double binds for any therapeutic situation.

Step One: *Structure a self-referential metalevel with highly motivating psychological implications.* In traditional hypnotherapy this is done directly by first discussing with patients all their personal reasons for wanting to deal with their problems before any formal induction of hypnosis. Much of the art in hypnotherapy is precisely in structuring metalevels via psychological implication. These metalevels often take the form of associational networks and frames of reference that contain highly motivating personal material of which patients are usually unaware. This highly motivating personal material functions as a lock structuring the tumblers of their associative processes and unconscious potentials in such a way that they will be "turned on" or actualized by the key therapeutic suggestions that are then presented at the opportune moment (Erickson & Rossi, 1979).

Step Two: *Offer two or more key therapeutic suggestions on the primary levels.* In this second step the hypnotherapeutic art is to tie these primary-level therapeutic alternatives to the metalevels of psychological implication in the many, diverse, and complex ways that are so typical of real clinical situations (Erickson, Rossi, & Rossi, 1976; Erickson & Rossi, 1979). The interactions between the metalevels of Step One and the therapeutic alternatives of Step Two are always multilevel, complex, circular, and recursive, as is characteristic of all nonlinear systems of mind (Bateson, 1972/1988).

Closing Comments

In this section we have attempted to clarify the difference between logical and psychological double binds. We have found that all published examples of hypnotic double binds use psychological implication to facilitate creative choice and therapeutic suggestions. We have differentiated between three levels of therapeutic double binds that are currently being developed in hypnosis:

(1) Cheek's psychophysiological and ideomotor responses;

(2) Rossi's intrapersonal response potentials; and

(3) Haley's interpersonal strategic therapy.

The art of formulating therapeutic double binds can be found in coordinating two interlocking mental levels:

(1) *a metalevel of psychological implication that*

(2) *structures hypnotic suggestions given on a primary level.*

In addition, we have explored Zen koans as transpersonal double binds that facilitate the experience of Enlightenment. From a Western perspective, Enlightenment is hypothesized to be a momentary breakthrough of the learned limitations characterizing the rational, dualistic "generalized reality orientation." A direction for future work is suggested in our brief exploration of how double binds may be inherent in all creative processes to the degree that they involve a breakdown of old frames of reference and a facilitation of new insights and patterns of consciousness.

TYPES OF DOUBLE BIND

	Haley	Rossi	Cheek	Zen
Area of Focus	Interpersonal	Intrapersonal	Psychophysiological	Transpersonal
Type of double bind	Paradoxical directive; double level messages for manipulating behavior	Conscious-unconscious double binds, learned limitations	Physiological to ideomotor and verbal level double binds	Koans: paradoxical directives that exclude rational mind processes
Process facilitated	Hypnotic challenges evoking involuntary hypnotic responses	Explores unique unconscious response tendencies	Explores physiological and ideomotor response tendencies	Experience of the Self
Therapist (Roshi) role	Strategic reorientation of patient's behavior	Facilitates creative choice and the patient's inner response potentials	Facilitates shift from physiological to verbal levels of response	Facilitates Samadhi
Descriptors of therapist (Roshi) role	Directive and authoritative	Permissive and exploratory	Directive and exploratory	Directive, exploratory, and authoritative
Purpose	Strategic directive therapy for human problems on interpersonal level	Facilitating creative choice, personality development, and human potentials	Facilitates symptom and trauma resolution	Enlightenment

A comparison of the Haley, Cheek, and Rossi formulations of the therapeutic double bind, together with the Zen koan as a form of transpersonal double bind.

Footnotes

Part I

1. Because this section is a verbatim transcription of the audiotape that accompanies this volume, grammatical errors and inconsistencies (Erickson's general use of the masculine pronoun and incorrect mixing of singular and plural pronouns and referents) remain as Erickson originally spoke them. This presentation was given to the San Diego Society of Clinical Hypnosis on May 10, 1964.
2. *See* "Naturalistic Techniques of Hypnosis" (Erickson, 1958/1980) and "Further Clinical Techniques of Hypnosis: Utilization Techniques" (Erickson, 1959/1980).
3. See Erickson, Rossi, & Rossi, 1976; Erickson & Rossi, 1979.
4. *See* Rossi, 1986; Rossi & Cheek, 1989; Rossi & Ryan, 1986.
5. *See* Izquierdo et al, 1988.
6. *See* Rossi, 1982, 1986a; Rossi & Cheek, 1989; Rossi & Nimmons, 1991.
7. *See* Erickson, 1948/1980.
8. *See* Lynn, Weeks, Matyi, & Neufeld, 1988; Stone & Lundy, 1988.
9. *See* Pratt, Wood, & Alman, 1988.
10. *See* Kazdin, 1982; Nugent, 1989.
11. Further illustrations and exercises for learning this approach can be found in Erickson, Rossi, & Rossi (1976) and in Erickson & Rossi (1979).
12. *See* Erickson, 1964b/1980.
13. *See* Erickson, 1948/1980.
14. *See* Erickson, 1967/1980.
15. *See* Erickson, 1964a/1980. Also note that this topic is usually indexed under the headings of *resistance* (discharging and displacing) and the *negative* in the Erickson/Rossi volumes, as well as the previous volumes of this series (Rossi/Ryan).
16. *See* Erickson & Rossi, 1977/1980.

Part II

1. *See* Erickson, Rossi & Rossi, 1976.
2. *See* Part V of Rossi & Ryan, 1985, for a detailed example of Erickson's trance work with a stutterer. Audio cassette of this demonstration accompanies volume.
3. *See* Rossi & Smith, 1990.
4. This case was published for the first time in Volume IV of Erickson, 1980. The original manuscript was dated "circa 1965."

5. *See* Erickson, 1963/1980, for a fascinating report on one of his most provocative cases.
6. *See* Erickson & Rossi, 1989.
7. Other examples of Erickson's use of shock and surprise with patients can be found in Rossi, 1973, and Erickson & Rossi, 1979. For a more general discussion of shock and creative moments, see Rossi, 1985. An interesting cultural variation of the use of shock and surprise in modulating consciousness can be found in the use of koans and other forms of shock in Zen training. This topic is explored in the final section of this volume.

Part III
1. An audiotape of this presentation was donated by Dr. Clancey Poor. The presentation was given on February 27, 1954, location unknown.
2. Erickson's two important papers in this area are "Naturalistic Techniques of Hypnosis" (1958/1989) and "Further Clinical Techniques of Hypnosis: Utilization Techniques" (1959/1980). *See* Erickson, Rossi, & Rossi (1976) for the theory, practice, and further examples of the "yes set."
3. *See* in particular, Rossi & Cheek, 1989.
4. *See* Libet, 1985.
5. *See* Rossi, 1988, 1989.

Part IV
1. Presentation given in Los Angeles on February 2, 1966, to the Southern California Society of Clinical Hypnosis.
2. *See* Erickson's early research on indirect trance induction by focusing on serial sensory processes in Volume I of Erickson, 1980c.
3. *See* Aldrich & Bernstein, 1987; Rossi, 1982, 1986a & b; Rossi & Cheek, 1988; Rossi & Nimmons, 1991.
4. *See* Lippincott, 1990; Rossi & Sing, 1990.
5 *See* Rossi, 1990a & b.
6. *See* Kandel, 1989.
7. *See* Erickson, Rossi, & Rossi (1976) and Erickson & Rossi (1979) for detailed examples of the Interspersal Technique

Part V
1. Presentation given in 1954, location unknown.

Part VI
1. Presentation given in 1967, location unknown.

2. *See* Rossi & Ryan, 1985, for a fuller description of this case (pp. 123-124).
3. *See* Part IX of *Volume I*, "Facilitating New Identity," in Erickson, 1980c, for many case examples of this approach.
4. *See* Erickson, 1980b, for a detailed account of this case.
5. *See* Erickson, Rossi, & Rossi, 1976, and Erickson & Rossi, 1980.
6. *See* Rossi, 1986b, 1991; Rossi & Cheek, 1989.
7. *See* Tsuji & Kobayashi, 1988.
8. *See* Aldrich & Bernstein, 1987.
9. *See* "Correcting an Inferiority Complex" in Erickson, 1980a.
10. *See* Rossi & Ryan, 1985, for a detailed presentation (including audio cassette) of Erickson's hypnotic work with a stutterer.
11. *See* Kandel & Schwartz, 1985.

Part VII
1. This section was written primarily by Patrick Jichaku who, at the time, was a Zen monk in training at the Los Angeles Zen Center. He is currently in a post-doctoral clinical internship program at UCLA's Neurospsychiatric Institute.

References

Aitken, R. (1978). *A Zen Wave*. Tokyo, Japan: Weatherhill.

Aldrich, K., & Bernstein, D. (1987). The effects of time of day on hypnotizability. *International Journal of Clinical and Experimental Hypnosis, 35*(3), 141-145.

Bateson, G. (1972/1988). *Steps to an Ecology of Mind*. New York: Ballantine.

Bateson, G., Jackson, D., Haley, J., & Weakland, J. (1956). Toward a theory of schizophrenia. *Behavioral Science, 1*, 251-264.

Berger, M. (1978). *Beyond the Double Bind: Communication and Family Systems, Theories, and Techniques with Schizophrenics*. New York: Brunner/Mazel.

Chandrasekhar, S. (1987). *Truth and Beauty: Aesthetics and Motivations in Science*. Chicago: University of Chicago Press.

Cheek, D. (1959). Unconscious perception of meaningful sounds during surgical anesthesia as revealed under hypnosis. *The American Journal of Clinical Hypnosis, 1*, 101-113.

Cheek, D. (1961). Value of ideomotor sex-determination technique of LeCron for uncovering subconscious fears in obstetric patients. *International Journal of Clinical & Experimental Hypnosis, 9*(4), 249-259.

Cheek, D. (1965). Some newer understandings of dreams in relation to threatened abortion and premature labor. *Pacific Medicine & Surgery*, 379-384.

Cheek, D. (1969). Communication with the critically ill. *The American Journal of Clinical Hypnosis, 12*(2), 75-85.

Cheek, D. (1974). Sequential head and shoulder movements appearing with age regression in hypnosis to birth. *The American Journal of Clinical Hypnosis, 16*, 261-266.

Cheek, D. (1975). Maladjustment patterns apparently related to imprinting at birth. *The American Journal of Clinical Hypnosis, 18*(2), 75-82.

Cheek, D. (1976). Short-term hypnotherapy for frigidity using exploration of early life attitudes. *The American Journal of Clinical Hypnosis, 19*(1), 20-27.

Cheek, D. (1979). Consideration of LeCron's ideomotor questioning methods. *Swedish Journal of Hypnosis*, August, 44-51.

Cheek, D. (1984). Unpublished personal communication on audiotape between David Cheek and Ernest Rossi on "the early days of hypnosis." February 13.

Erickson, M. (1948/1980). Hypnotic psychotherapy. In E. Rossi (Ed.), *The Collected Papers of Milton H. Erickson on Hypnosis. Vol. IV. Innovative Hypnotherapy* (pp. 35–48). New York: Irvington.

Erickson, M. (1952/1980). Deep hypnosis and its induction. In E. Rossi (Ed.), *The Collected Papers of Milton H. Erickson on Hypnosis. Vol. I. The Nature of Hypnosis and Suggestion* (pp. 139-167). New York: Irvington.

Erickson, M. (1958/1980). Naturalistic techniques of hypnosis. In E. Rossi (Ed.), *The Collected Papers of Milton H. Erickson on Hypnosis. Vol. I. The Nature of Hypnosis and Suggestion* (pp. 168-176). New York: Irvington.

Erickson, M. (1959/1980). Further clinical techniques of hypnosis: Utilization techniques. In E. Rossi (Ed.), *The Collected Papers of Milton H. Erickson on Hypnosis. Vol. I. The Nature of Hypnosis and Suggestion* (pp. 177-205). New York: Irvington.

Erickson, M. (1961/1980). Historical note on the hand levitation and other ideomotor techniques. In E. Rossi (Ed.), *The Collected Papers of Milton H. Erickson on Hypnosis. Vol. I. The Nature of Hypnosis and Suggestion* (pp. 135-138). New York: Irvington.

Erickson, M. (1963/1980). Hypnotically oriented psychotherapy in organic brain damage. In E. Rossi (Ed.), *The Collected Papers of Milton H. Erickon on Hypnosis. Vol. IV. Innovative Hypnotherapy* (pp. 283-311).

Erickson, M. (1964a/1980). An hypnotic technique for resistant patients: The patient, the technique, and its rationale and field experiments. In E. Rossi (Ed.), *The Collected Papers of Milton H. Erickson on Hypnosis. Vol. I. The*

Nature of Hypnosis and Suggestion (pp. 299-330). New York: Irvington.

Erickson, M. 1964b/1980). The confusion technique in hypnosis. In E. Rossi (Ed.), *The Collected Papers of Milton H. Erickson on Hypnosis. Vol. I. The Nature of Hypnosis and Suggestion* (pp. 258-291). New York: Irvington.

Erickson, M. (1967/1980). Further experimental investigation of hypnosis: Hypnotic and nonhypnotic realities. In E. Rossi (Ed.), *The Collected Papers of Milton H. Erickson on Hypnosis. Vol. I. The Nature of Hypnosis and Suggestion* (pp. 18-82). New York: Irvington.

Erickson, M. (1980a). Correcting an inferiority complex. In E. Rossi (Ed.), *The Collected Papers of Milton H. Erickson on Hypnosis. Volume IV. Innovative Hypnotherapy* (pp. 491-498). New York: Irvington.

Erickson, M. (1980b). Facilitating a new cosmetic frame of reference. In E. Rossi (Ed.), *The Collected Papers of Milton H. Erickson on Hypnosis. Volume IV. Innovative Hypnotherapy* (pp. 465-469). New York: Irvington.

Erickson, M. (1980c). *The Collected Papers of Milton H. Erickson on Hypnosis (4 Vols)*. Edited by Ernest Rossi. New York: Irvington.

Volume I: *The Nature of Hypnosis and Suggestion*

Volume II: *Hypnotic Alteration of Sensory, Perceptual and Psychophysical Processes*

Volume III: *Hypnotic Investigation of Psychodynamic Processes*

Volume IV: *Innovative Hypnotherapy.*

Erickson, M., Haley, J., & Weakland, J. (1959). A transcript of a trance induction with commentary. In E. Rossi (Ed.), *The Collected Papers of Milton H. Erickson on Hypnosis. Vol. I. The Nature of Hypnosis and Suggestion* (pp. 206-257). New York: Irvington.

Erickson, M., & Rossi, E. (1975/1980). Varieties of double bind. In E. Rossi (Ed.), *The Collected Papers of Milton H. Erickson on Hypnosis. Vol. I. The Nature of Hypnosis and Suggestion* (pp. 412-429). New York: Irvington.

Erickson, M., & Rossi, E. (1977/1980). Autohypnotic experiences of Milton H. Erickson. In E. Rossi (Ed.), *The Col-*

lected Papers of Milton H. Erickson on Hypnosis. Vol. I.
The Nature of Hypnosis and Suggestion (pp. 108-132).
New York: Irvington.

Erickson, M., & Rossi, E. (1979). *Hypnotherapy: An Exploratory Casebook*. New York: Irvington.

Erickson, M., & Rossi, E. (1980). The indirect forms of suggestion. In E. Rossi (Ed.), *The Collected Papers of Milton H. Erickson on Hypnosis. Vol. I. The Nature of Hypnosis and Suggestion* (pp. 452-477). New York: Irvington.

Erickson, M., & Rossi, E. (1981). *Experiencing Hypnosis: Therapeutic Approaches to Altered States*. New York: Irvington.

Erickson, M., & Rossi, E. (1989). *The February Man: Evolving Consciousness and Identity in Hypnotherapy*. New York: Brunner/Mazel.

Erickson, M., Rossi, E., & Rossi, S. (1976). *Hypnotic Realities*. New York: Irvington.

Hakuun, Yasutani Roshi. (1973). The crisis in human affairs and the liberation found in Buddhism. *Zen Center of Los Angeles Journal, 3*(3-4), 36-47.

Haley, J. (1963). *Strategies of Psychotherapy*. New York: Grune & Stratton.

Haley, J. (1973). *Uncommon Therapy*. New York: W. W. Norton.

Haley, J. (1976). Development of a theory: A history of a research project. In C. Sluzki & D. Ransom (Eds.), *Double Bind* (pp. 59-104). New York: Grune & Stratton.

Haley, J. (1982). The contribution to therapy of Milton H. Erickson. In J. Zeig (Ed.), *Ericksonian Approaches to Hypnosis and Psychotherapy*. New York: Brunner/Mazel.

Izquierdo, I., Netto, C., Chaves, M., Dalmaz, C., Pereira, M. Ferreira, N., & Siegfried, B. (1988). The organization of memory into "files." In J. Delacour & J. Levy (Eds.), *Systems with Leaning and Memory Abilities*. Amsterdam: Elsevier Science Books.

Jung, C. (1953). *Two Essays on Analytical Psychology. Vol. VII. The Collected Works of C. G. Jung.* (R. F. C. Hull,

Trans.). Bollingen Series XX: Princeton, New Jersey: Princeton University Press.

Jung, C. (1960). *The Structure and Dynamics of the Psyche. Vol. III. The Collected Works of C. G. Jung.* (R. F. C. Hull, Trans.). Bollingen Series XX. Princeton, New Jersey: Princeton University Press.

Kandel, E. (1989). Genes, nerve cells, and the remembrance of things past. *Journal of Neuropsychiatry, 1*, 103-125.

Kandel, E., & Schwartz, G. (1985). *Principles of Neural Science* (2nd Ed.). New York: Elsevier.

Kasulis, T. (1981). *Zen Action/Zen Person*. Honolulu: University Press of Hawaii.

Kazdin, A. (1982). *Single Case Research Designs*. New York: Oxford University Press.

LeCron, L. (1954). A hypnotic technique for uncovering unconscious material. *Journal of Clinical & Experimental Hypnosis, 2*, 76-79.

Libet, B. (1985). Unconscious cerebral initiative and the role of conscious will in voluntary action. *The Behavioral and Brain Sciences, 8*(4), 529-539.

Lippincott, B. (1990). An experimental assessment of the ultradian theory of clinical hypnosis. Paper presented at the 32nd Annual Scientific Meeting of The American Society of Clinical Hypnosis, March 27, 1990.

Lynn, S., Weeks, J., Matyi, C., & Neufeld, V. (1988). Direct versus indirect suggestions, archaic involvement, and hypnotic experience. *Journal of Abnormal Psychology, 93*(3), 296-301.

McGaugh, J. (1983). Preserving the presence of the past: Hormonal influences on memory storage. *American Psychologist, 38*(2), 161-173.

Nugent, W. (1989). Evidence concerning the causal effect of an Ericksonian hypnotic intervention. In S. Lankton (Ed.), *Ericksonian Monographs. Vol. 5. Ericksonian Hypnosis: Application, Preparation, and Research*. New York: Brunner/Mazel.

Pratt, G., Wood, D., & Alman, B. (1988). *A Clinical Hypnosis Primer*. New York: Wiley.

Ravitz, L. (1950). Electrometric correlates of the hypnotic states. *Science, 112*, 341-342.

Rosenzweig, M. (1984). Experience, memory, and the brain. *American Psychologist, 39*, 365-376.

Rossi, E. (1972/1985). *Dreams and the Growth of Personality (2nd Ed.)*. New York: Brunner/Mazel.

Rossi, E. (1973). Psychological shocks and creative moments in psychotherapy. *The American Journal of Clinical Hypnosis, 16*, 9-22. (Also in Erickson, 1980c, Vol. IV, pp. 447-464.)

Rossi, E. (1982). Hypnosis and ultradian cycles: A new state(s) theory of hypnosis? *The American Journal of Clinical Hypnosis, 25*(1), 21-32.

Rossi, E. (1986a). Altered states of consciousness in everyday life: The ultradian rhythms. In B. Wolman (Ed.), *Handbook of Altered States of Consciousness* (pp. 97-132). New York: Van Nostrand.

Rossi, E. (1986b). *The Psychobiology of Mind-Body Healing: New Concepts of Therapeutic Hypnosis*. New York: W. W. Norton.

Rossi, E. (1988). Paradoxes of time, consciousness, and free will: Integrating Bohm, Jung, and Libet on ethics. *Psychological Perspectives, 19*(1), 50-55.

Rossi, E. (1989). Chaos, determinism, and free will. *Psychological Perspectives, 20*(1), 110-127.

Rossi, E. (1990). The new yoga of the west. *Psychological Perspectives,* Issue 22.

Rossi, E. (1991). *The Twenty-Minute Break: The Ultradian Healing Response*. Los Angeles: Tarcher.

Rossi, E., & Cheek, D. (1988). *Mind-Body Therapy: Ideodynamic Healing in Hypnosis*. New York: W. W. Norton.

Rossi, E., & Ryan, M. (Eds.) (1985). *Life Reframing in Hypnosis. Vol. II. The Seminars, Workshops, and Lectures of Milton H. Erickson*. New York: Irvington.

Rossi, E., & Ryan, M. (Eds.) (1986). *Mind-Body Communication in Hypnosis. Vol. III. The Seminars, Workshops, and Lectures of Milton H. Erickson*. New York: Irvington.

Rossi, E., Ryan, M., & Sharp, F. (Eds.) (1983). *Healing in Hypnosis. Vol. I. The Seminars, Workshops, and Lectures of Milton H. Erickson.* New York: Irvington.

Rossi, E., & Sing, H. (1990). A clinical-experimental assessment of the ultradian theory of clinical hypnosis. Paper presented at the 32nd Annual Scientific Meeting of The American Society of Clinical Hypnosis, March 27, 1990.

Rossi, E., & Smith, M. (1990). The eternal quest: Hidden rhythms of stress and healing in everyday life." *Psychological Perspectives*, Issue 22, 6-23.

Shor, R. (1959). Hypnosis and the concept of the generalized reality orientation. *American Journal of Psychotherapy, 13*, 582-602.

Siegel, B. (1989). *Peace, Love, and Healing.* New York: Harper & Row.

Sluzki, C., & Ransom, D. (1979). *Double Bind.* New York: Grune & Stratton.

Sluzki, C., & Vernon, E. (1976). The double bind as a universal pathogenic situation. In C. Sluzki & D. Ransom (Eds.), *Double Bind.* New York: Grune & Stratton.

Stone, J., & Lundy, R. (1988). Behavioral compliance with direct and indirect body movement suggestion. *Journal of Abnormal Psychology, 94*(3), 256-263.

Thilly, F., & Wood, L. (1941). *History of Philosophy.* New York: Holt & Co.

Tsuji, Y., & Kobayashi, T. (1988). Short and long ultradian EEG components in daytime arousal. *Electroencephalography and Clinical Neurophysiology, 70*, 110-117.

Watzlawick, P. (1982). Erickson's contribution to the interactional view of psychotherapy. In J. Zeig (Ed.), *Ericksonian Approaches to Hypnosis and Psychotherapy* (pp. 147-154). New York: Brunner/Mazel.

Watzlawick, P., Weakland, J., & Fisch, R. (1974). *Change.* New York: W. W. Norton.

Weakland, J. (1982). Erickson's contribution to the double bind. In J. Zeig (Ed.), *Ericksonian Approaches to Hypnosis and Psychotherapy* (pp. 163-170). New York: Brunner/Mazel.

Whitehead, A., & Russell, B. (1910). *Principia Mathematica*. Cambridge: Cambridge University Press.

Wilber, K. (1980). *The Atman Project: A Transpersonal View of Human Development*. Wheaton, Illinois: Theosophical Publishing House.

Wilber, K. (1981). *No Boundary: Eastern and Western Approaches to Personal Growth*. Boulder, Colorado: Shambhala.

Yamada, K. (1979). *Gateless Gate*. Los Angeles: Center Publishing.

Yampolski, P. (Trans.) (1971). *The Zen Master Hakuin: Selected Writings*. New York: Columbia University Press.

Index

"Abaissement du niveau mental" 165

Acceptance set 148

Aggression, redirecting 199-201

Aitken, R. 246

Alexia 120

Amnesia
  blanket 15
  choosing 3-5
  hypnotic 14-16
  nonhypnotic (everyday) 14-16, 20-22, 226
  traumatic 16-20

Analogy 131

Anesthesia
  Cesarean, example 21-22
  Cheek's view of 239
  dissociation and 20-22
  indirect 28, 29-30
  learning via 46-47
  questions evoking 57-61
  "saddle block" 59, 60, 62

Anger (provoking recovery) 118-121

Anxiety
  aging and 187-192
  chronic habits and 185-187
  concealing real symptoms 187-195

Aphasia 118

Associations (associative processes)
  ideodynamic 145-148
  implication and 235, 248
  irrational 214-217
  processes 147-148

therapeutic/transpersonal double binds and 248-249

Attention
  distracting 23, 130, 193-195
  dividing 3
  fixating (focusing) 3, 5, 10-11, 19, 130, 162-163
  hypnosis vs. everyday life 2
  induction and 5-6
  minimizing movement 10-11
  redirecting 131
  trance without awareness 99-102

Attitude(s)
  competency vs. omnipotency 103-104
  confidence 103, 112
  facilitating hypnosis 42-43, 61
  metaphor and 110
  reframing illness/injury 211-217
  therapeutic 102-104

Autogenic training 45-47, 49

Autohypnosis
  patient's 81
  therapist's 8-10

Automatic writing 237

Bacon, F. 6

Basic Rest-Activity Cycle 165

Bateson, G. x, 225, 230, 232, 234, 235, 236, 242, 247, 248

Behavior(al)
  double-binding questions and 150

hypnosis and 33
ideomotor triad 237, 250
inevitabilities 182-185, 208
interrelationship with
    hypnosis 211-214
multiple levels of 22-24
obsessive-compulsive,
    reversing 202-204
problems 108-109
reinforcing 45-47
self-reference, common
    denominator of 225
utilizing spontaneous 151-
    152
Berger, M. 227
Bernheim, H. 32
Body
    illness/injury and 211-214
    minimal cues of (*see also*
        separate listing) 114,
        116-117, 125
    processes and trance 144
    respect for 105-106, 211-214
BRAC 165
Brain injury 196-197
"Breaking point" 217
Breast cancer 193-195
Catalepsy 44, 45, 57-61, 226,
    235, 236
Catharsis 122-125, 130
Cerebral palsy 199-201
Cerebrovascular injury 118-121
Challenge(s) 159-162, 173, 232,
    233, 234, 237, 250
Charcot, J. 165
Cheek, D. 231, 236-239, 242,
    250
Children
    choice and 209
    double bind and 209
    play and 150, 225
    rapport and 130-131

therapeutic binds and 149
Choice
    Erickson-Rossi double bind
        and 240-242, 250
    hypnosis and ix, 65
    illusory vs. creative (free) xi,
        xii-xiv
    schizophrenic and 242
    students and 209-210
    therapeutic/transpersonal
        double bind and 248-
        249
Cigarette smoking 185-187, 190-
    191
Claustrophobia
    demonstration of subject with
        72-93
    spatial relationships in 84-
        86, 88, 92
Colitis, ulcerative 105-106
Comfort 17, 163-166, 176-177,
    181, 208
"Common Everyday Trance"
    114-116, 165
Communication
    conscious vs. unconscious
        185-192
    of ideas 1, 109-110
    influence 236
    meta- 131
    two-level 21-22, 76, 227
Comparative (comparison) 151,
    163-166
Complexes
    "feeling-toned" 12
    inferiority, depotentiating
        220-221
Conditioned response 57
Confusion 49-51, 202-204, 227
Conscious(ness)
    self 68, 70

vs. unconscious xiii, 100-102, 185-192
Context of problem 117-118
Conversation, casual 104-105
Coronary 218-219
Covering all possibilities 144
Creative moments 231
Cure
    chain smoking, suspicion of 187
    lessening vs. 77, 86
    patient's credit for 214-217
    "secret" 98-102
Defenses
    ego 106-107
    nature of 106-107
    as resistance 98-102, 130
Dental problem 192
Depersonalization 24-31
Depression 205, 231
Diagnosis 126-128
Dissociation
    anesthesia and 20-22
    facilitating 163-166
    self and 24, 25
Double bind x-xiv
    cerebral palsy patient and 199-201
    characteristics of 227
    conscious-unconscious 238, 241, 250
    creative 159-162, 231
    dentistry and 208
    Erickson's use of x, 232, 234, 238
    ethics of xi, xii, 202, 241
    everyday uses of 201
    frigidity and 202-204
    hypnosis and 225
    interpersonal aspects of 232-233, 244, 250

intrapersonal aspects of 239-242, 245, 250
    learning, facilitating 209-210
    logical (see Logical double bind as separate listing)
    misusing 202
    pathologic 230
    play as 150
    premature ejaculation and 202-204
    psychological (see Psychological double bind as separate listing)
    redirecting aggression 199-201
    reorienting symptom/problem 199-201
    resistance, utilizing 209-210
    salesman's use of 201
    schizophrenic 225-227, 240-242
    therapeutic xi, xii, xiv, 128-130, 150, 199-201, 225, 230, 240-242, 248-249
    transpersonal (see Transpersonal double bind as separate listing)
    two-level 208, 227
    Zen koan as 242-247
Doubt 182-185, 204, 247
Dreams 12-14
Dualism (dualistic thinking) 243, 244, 245, 246, 249
Emotions, phobic 87-93
Emphysema 99-102
Enlightenment
    schizophrenia vs. 242
    transpersonal double bind and 243-247, 250
Epilepsy 180-182, 184
Erickson('s), M. x, xi

double bind, use of (*see also* separate listing) 232, 234, 238
father's death at 97 218-219
hallucination and 226, 235
ideomotor techniques 237, 250
implication and hypnotherapy 147-148, 248
indirect methods 4, 28-30, 51, 102, 111, 130-131, 148, 152-154, 162-163, 167-171, 177-180, 234, 237, 240
neurology, modern and 223
observational skills 113-116, 126-128
-Rossi exploratory double bind 239-242
as transition figure x
wheelchair learnings 222
Expectancy
facilitating hypnosis 42-43, 111
premature ejaculation and 204
therapist's knowledge 103
Eye closure 154-155, 175-176, 241
Facilitation (facilitating) (*See also* Utilization)
double bind as (*see also* Psychological double bind) 209-210
dreams 12-14
hypnosis (*see also* separate listing) 42-43, 163-166
mental activity 10-11
Family therapy, strategic 232-236, 250
Fear 87-93, 217-218
"Feeling-toned complexes" 12

Feelings
altering 72-74
concealing 192
extending 163-166
phobic 87-93
trance and 144
wondering about 162-163
Fisch, R. 236
Free association 32-33
Free will xiii
Freud, S. 32, 33
Future
orientations 144, 149
perhaps 145-148
General Adaptation Syndrome 17
Goal-setting 204-206
Hakuin's story 246-247
Hakuun, Y. 244
Haley, J. xi, 225, 231, 232-236, 237, 242, 250
Hallucination
accepting 36
spontaneous 226, 236
"stopped seeing" 57-61
Hand/arm levitation 47, 56, 67, 116-117
Handedness 65-69
Hegel 245
Hemorrhage
cerebral 219
gastric 206-208
Hiccups 214-217
"Hobson's Choice" 154-155
Humor 74
Hypermnesia 46-47
Hypnosis (hypnotic) (*See also* Hypnotic phenomena; Trance)
attitudes facilitating 42-43
authoritarian vs. permissive x, 51, 162-163, 195, 232, 236, 237, 240-242, 250

as behavior 33
"black art" of 159-162
choice in ix, 65
communication of ideas 1,
    21-22, 109-110, 126
demonstrations 43-50, 52-
    60, 65-72, 72-93
direct vs. indirect induction
    of 5, 102, 152-154
double bind and (*see also*
    separate listing) 225-227
everyday life and 1-3, 19
expectancy in 42-43, 111
"hypnotic psychotherapy,"
    definition of 29
"hypnotic susceptibility" 51
indirect vs. non-directive 43
as influence communication
    236
interrelationship of 211-214
koans and 247
manipulation in (*see also*
    separate listing) 37-40,
    156-157
"Neuro-psycho-physiologi-
    cal" foundations of 27,
    30, 239
potentials and 218-219
protecting the patient 61-65
psychoanalysis and 32-33
psychophysiological, Cheek's
    model of 236-239, 250
technique, learning 162-163
telephone 182-185
temporal considerations in
    112-113
touch and 32
utilization (*see* separate
    listing)
Hypnotic phenomena (*See also*
    Hypnosis; Trance)
    amnesia (*see also* separate
    listing) 3-5, 14-16
    anesthesia (*see* separate
    listing)
    automatic writing 237
    catalepsy 44, 45, 57-61, 226,
        235, 236
    depersonalization 24-31
    dissociation 20-22, 24, 25,
        163-166
    eye closure 154-155, 175-
        176, 241
    hallucination 36, 57-61, 226,
        236
    hand/arm levitation 47, 56,
        67, 116-117
    hypermnesia 46-47
    ideomotor signaling 111,
        236-239, 241
    implication facilitating (*see*
        separate listing)
    literalism 49-51
    minimal cues of (*see* separate
        listing)
    questions facilitating (*see*
        separate listing)
    resistance and (*see* separate
        listing)
    suggestion and (*see* separate
        listing)
    time distortion (*see* separate
        listing)
Hypnotizability 106-107
Identity
    depersonalization of 26-31
    shifting of 125-126
Ideodynamic processes 145-148
Ideomotor (processes)
    Cheek's double bind 236-
        239, 250
    signaling 111, 236-239, 241,
        250

Illness
    body and 211-217
    joy and 218
    reframing 211-217
    restricting 218-219
    terminal 217-218
    utilizing 221-223
Illusion of adjustment 185-187
Implication 4, 49, 50, 111
    comparative and 151-152
    double binds and 148, 154-155
    "Hobson's Choice" 154-155
    psychological double bind and 231, 232, 233, 234, 235, 236, 248-249
    therapeutic use of 145-148
    transpersonal double bind and 248-249
Inner resources 116
Interspersal technique 169-171, 173-177
Intonation (inflection) (*See* Vocal cues)
Izquierdo, I. 18
Jackson, D. 225
Janet, P. 32, 165
Jung, C. 12, 245
Kasulis, T. 246
Kazdin, A. 31
Koan 225, 242-247, 249, 250
Kubie, L. x
Language
    brain injury and 196-197
    verbal and nonverbal cues for 116-117, 152-154, 168
    violence, utilizing 195-196
    vocal cues (intonation, inflection) 6, 116-117, 167-167, 173-177, 187-192
Lashley's rat research 120

Learned limitations xiv, 130, 240, 244, 245, 247, 249, 250
Learning
    double bind facilitating 209-210
    textbook vs. real life 109-110
LeCron, L. 237
Libet, B. xiii
Literalism 49-51
Logic vs. illogic 33-37
Logical double bind 227-229, 234
    Figure 1 228
    Figure 2 229
    Figure 3 229, 236
    metalevel statement 228, 229, 236, 240-242
    primary-level statement 228, 229, 240-242
    psychological double bind and 235, 243, 248
    transpersonal double bind and 243
Manipulation
    creative choice vs. authoritarian 98, 156, 195, 232, 236, 250
    Erickson's use of 97-98, 156
    ethics of 37-40, 156
    Haley's analysis of 236
    hypnosis and 37-40, 41, 65
    observation vs. 114-116, 126-128
    psychoanalysis and 37-40
    reframing 156
McGaugh, J. 239
Mead, M. 7
Meaning, multiple levels of 6, 56, 154-155, 169-171
Memory(ies)
    electroshock and 18-20

ideomotor triad of 237
psychophysiological levels of
    239
reviewing 49
state-dependent 16-20, 239
surgical 237
traumatic 16-20, 237, 239
ultradian rhythms and 166
Menopause 110
Mental mechanisms x
Metacommunication 131
Metalevels 169-171, 173-177
Metaphor
    attention 131
    facilitating menopause 110
    terminal illness and 217-218
Migraine headache 205
Minimal cues 5
    body 6, 114
    conscious vs. unconscious
        communication 185-192
    emotional complex and 12
    meaning and 6, 56, 154-155,
        169-171
    perceiving 11-12, 45-47
    of trance induction 65-68
    vocal 6, 116-117, 167-167,
        173-177, 187-192
Mu 246
Negative 68-72, 98-102, 128-
    130, 209-210, 214-217
Neurology, modern 223
"Neuro-psycho-physiological"
    27, 30, 239
Not knowing 98-102, 148
Nugent, W. 31
Nurses, important role of 169-
    171
Obesity (See also Weight loss)
    173-180
Observation
    diagnosis and 126-128

double leg amputation
    example 126-128
    Erickson's skill at 113-116
    manipulation vs. 114-116
Obsessive-compulsive behavior
    202-204, 206-208
Or 149
Orthopedic injury 159-173
Pain
    directing 171-173
    indirect approaches to 177-
        180
    learning relief for 173-180
    orthopedic 159-173, 182-185
    "plain speaking" and 166-
        167
    provoking relief 171-173
    reverse suggestions for relief
        of 167-168
    sciatic 173-177, 184
    time distortion and 41, 173-
        177
Paradox(ical)
    authoritarian-permissive x,
        51, 195
    conflict in double bind 227,
        244
    directive 232, 250, 250
    Epimenides 229, 234, 236
    koan as 243
    logical double bind and 228,
        234, 235
    pathological mechanisms
        202-204
    psychological double bind
        and 230, 232, 234,
    resistance and 167-168
    symptom prescription 180-
        182
    trance and 230
    transpersonal double bind
        and 243, 244

269

Paranoia 197
Pauses
    conveying ideas 168, 175
    trauma and use of 23
Perceptions
    altering 72-75
    exploring phobic 82-87
Perhaps 145-148
Personality
    aggressive 200-201
    illusion of 185-187
    therapist's 7-10
Phobia(s)
    claustrophobia (*see* separate
      listing)
    controlling 87-93
    emotions of 87-93
    fear 87-93, 217-218
    intellect in 91-93
    reorienting 199
    thinking and doing 76-82
Play 150
Positive
    converting negative into
      214-217
    juxtaposing with negative
      209-210
Posthypnotic suggestion (*See also*
    Suggestion) 57-61, 209-210,
    214-217
Provocation 118-121
Psychoanalysis
    hypnosis and 32-33
    manipulation and 37-40
Psychological double bind 230-
    242
    Cheek's ideomotor 236-239
    Figure 4 233
    Figure 5 234
    Figure 6 234, 235, 236
    Figure 7 238
    Figure 8 241

    Haley's interpersonal 232-
      236
    implication, unverbalized
      233, 234, 235, 236, 238
    logical double bind and 235,
      248
    Rossi's exploratory
      (intrapersonal) 239-242
    structuring 248-249
    trance and 230
Psychosis ("nude young men")
    34-36
Questions
    attention and 162-163
    double-binding 150, 154-155
    fail-safe 60
    indirect 152-154
    inducing/reinducing trance
      47-49, 57-61, 65, 66, 98-
      102
    negative and 68-72
    open-ended 43-45, 57-61
    pain, descriptions of 160
    permissive 154-155, 237
Ransom, D. 227
Rape 123
Rapport, children and 130-131
Ravitz, L. 49
Reality orientation 2, 244, 249
"Reassociate and reorganize" 27-
    31, 50-51
Recursion 229, 231, 238, 239,
    245-248
Reframing 105-106, 156, 211-
    217
Relaxation
    epilepsy and 181
    example of 122-123
    training 57-61, 176
    verbal and nonverbal cues for
      116-117, 152-154, 168

Resentment 163-166
Resistance
    defense and 98-102
    demonstrating 52, 53, 68-72,
        74
    depotentiating (utilizing) 98-
        102, 104-105, 130-131,
        159-162, 163-166, 167-
        168, 169-171, 195, 214-
        217
    humor and 74
    pain and 159-162
    paradox and 167-168
    parents' 95-98
    psychoanalysis and 38, 39
    resentment 163-166, 171
    salesman's use of 201
    symptomatology and 75
Response(iveness)
    involuntary, hypnotic 234,
        238
    many possibilities of 46-47
    unconscious tendencies 250
Reward 61, 62
Rhythm
    circadian 165
    entrainment of 165-166
    ultradian 23-24, 164-166
    utilizing 154
Rosenzweig, M. 239
Roshi 245, 246-247, 250
Rossi, E. x, xi, xii, xiii, 147, 231,
    234, 237, 238, 239-242, 248,
    250
Russell, B. 228
Samadhi 246, 250
Scapegoating as therapeutic 172
Schizophrenia
    double bind and 225-227
    enlightenment and 242
Secrets 101-102, 128-130
Self-consciousness 68, 70

Self-defeatism 204-206
Self-derogation 36-37
Self-enjoyment 221
Self-identity 122-125
Self-motivation 209-210
Self-reference (self-referential)
        225
    logical double binds 228,
        234
    messages 226
    psychological double binds
        231, 234, 248-249
    transpersonal double binds
        243, 248-249
Self-report 162-163
Self-responsibility 96-98, 99
Self-satisfaction 206-208
Selye, H. 17
Sensations
    phobic, exploring 82-87
    sexual (see also separate
        listing) 203
Sex(ual)
    frigidity 202-204
    incompatibility 187-192
    premature ejaculation 202-
        204
Shock 214-217
Shor, R. 244
Siegel, B. 223
Slang vs. obscene 123-125
Sluzki, C. 227, 231
Smoking 98-102
Sneezing fits 193-195
Somatic (See Body)
Somnambulism 166-167
Speech therapy 197
Spiegel, H. xii
Stage fright, overcoming 52-60
State-dependent (See Memory)
Stress 165

Stuttering
control vs. re-education 107-
108
correcting via infantile
sounds 220-221
reframing 220-221
Suggestion
amnesia and 15
comparative as 151-152
confusion and 202-204
covering all possibilities of
response 145-148, 149
direct vs. indirect x, 28-31,
51, 152-154, 237
double-binding (*see* Double
binds)
epilepsy and 180-182
Erickson's definition of 27-
30
facial cues and 177-180
fail-safe 145-148
future-oriented 144
implication and (*see also*
separate listing) 147-
148, 151-152
indirect forms of 4, 30, 111,
148, 162-163, 167-168,
169-171, 177-180, 237,
240
interspersing 169-171, 173-
177
manipulation as 156
multiple meaning of words
154-155
or as 149
pain and (*see* separate listing)
paradoxical 180-182, 202-
204
perhaps as 145-148
phrasing 104-105, 152, 170,
173-180
posthypnotic 57-61, 209-
210, 214-217

as psychobiological process
165, 214-217
questions as (*see* separate
listing)
reassociating and reorganizing 27-31
researching 30-31, 152, 169
reverse 167-168
sensitivity vs. 116
therapeutic/transpersonal
double bind and 248-
249
time-binding 202-204
Surprise 214-217
Symptom(atology)
context of 117-118
hiccups 214-217
as maneuver 106-107
prescription 167-168, 171-
173, 180-182
reframing 105-106, 211-214
resistance and 75
state of mind and 75-76
words and 214-217
Synthesis (Hegelian) 245
Then 154-155
Therapist('s)
autohypnosis 8-10
"Bulldog's" experience 8-10
double bind and 202
goal-setting and 204-206
as human being 123
personality 7-10
self-defeating patient and
204-206
suggestion, giving of 173-
177
techniques and 7-10
vulnerability 104-105
working with patients 13
Thilly, F. 245

Thinking
  objective vs. subjective 76-
    84, 86, 92
  phobic, exploring 82-87
"Thusness" 244
Time distortion
  facilitating 166-167
  hypnotic use of 40-41, 46-47
  pain and 41
  trance induction and 41, 98-
    102
Touch 32, 56, 71
Trance (therapeutic) (*See also*
    Hypnosis; Hypnotic phe-
    nomena)
  awakening 47
  behavioral inevitability and
    182-185
  as contest 98, 100
  deepening 151-152, 166-167
  indicators 113-116
  inducing/re-inducing 41, 47-
    49, 162-163
  jokes in 182-185
  minimal cues of (*see* separate
    listing)
  nursery rhymes and 146
  psychological double binds
    and 230
  questions inducing 44-45,
    47-49, 68-72, 98-102
  ratifying 47
  resistance to (*see* separate
    listing)
  somnambulistic 166-167
  "special psychological state"
    27, 50
  without awareness 98-102,
    116, 149
Transformation 116
Transpersonal double bind 242-
  250

Figure 9 243
Figure 10 244
koan as 242-249
structuring 248-249
Trauma
  accessing 16-18
  circumventing 18-20
  ideomotor triad and 237,
    238, 250
  resting from 23
  state-dependent memory and
    16-20, 239
Truisms 4, 102, 214-217
Two-level communication 76,
  227
Ulcer 206-208
Ultradian rhythms 23-24, 164-
  166, 239
Unconscious (processes)
  conscious vs. xiii, 100-102,
    185-192
  distractions (patients') 193-
    195
  free will and xiii
  nature of 182-185
  suggestion facilitating 173-
    177
  therapy and 4
Utilization (utilizing) (*See also*
    Facilitation)
  aggression 199-201
  amnesia, structuring 14-16
  autogenic training 45-47, 49
  behavior, spontaneous 151-
    152
  double bind and (*see also*
    separate listing) 209-210
  everyday life phenomena 1,
    14-16, 19
  handicaps 221-223
  history of patient 18-20
  illness 221-223

indirect 31, 148
manipulation (*see also*
    separate listing) 40, 156
motivations 52-57
natural processes 62-63
programming vs. x, 30, 51
provocation 118-121
resistance (*see also* separate
    listing) 39, 95-98, 209-
    210
responses 13-14, 145-148
therapist's personality 9
Verbal
    cues 116-117, 152-154
    ideomotor triad and 237,
        238, 239, 250
    vs. nonverbal 6-7
    violence, utilizing 195-196
Vernon, E. 231
Vocal cues (intonation, inflection)
    6, 116-117, 167-167, 173-
    177, 187-192
Vulgarity 122-125
Watzlawick, P. 236
Weakland, J. 225, 232, 236
Weight loss 177-180, 182-185
Whitehead, A. 228
Wilbur, K. 245
Wonder 150, 162-163
Wood, L. 245
Yamada, K. 246
Yampolski, P. 246
Yes set 4, 176, 214-217
"*Zeitgebers*" 166
Zen 148, 225, 242-247, 250

NOW AVAILABLE FROM IRVINGTON

The Wisdom of Milton H. Erickson
Volume 1, Hypnosis & Hypnotherapy

Ronald A. Havens, Editor

The psychiatrist Milton Erickson was a master hypnotist, capable of inducing trances by the most unexpected means—even a mere handshake. Erickson also published numerous books, articles, transcripts, and audiotapes. Erickson's books have sold more than 250,000 copies. *The Wisdom of Milton H. Erickson I: Hypnosis and Hypnotherapy* is the first work to provide a unified survey of the philosophy behind Erickson's techniques.

The material in this volume has been selected from the psychiatrist's lectures, seminars, articles, and books and is carefully organized to offer a clear account of how Erickson conceived of hypnosis, particularly its access to the unconscious and its role in the process of psychotherapy. The reader discovers what hypnosis actually does, explores general considerations on inducing the state, learns specific techniques, and most importantly, comes to understand the contribution that hypnosis can make in the healing or therapeutic process. *The Wisdom of Milton H. Erickson I: Hypnosis and Hypnotherapy* is a valuable guide to the work of one of psychiatry's most original and innovative minds.

...a heroic effort to bring clarity to a hard-to-grasp theory...(This book) is a major reference for students and scholars who want to know what Erickson said and when and where he said it.
Contemporary Psychology

ISBN 0-8290-2413-1 (Paper)
298 pages
$14.95

IRVINGTON PUBLISHERS, INC.
740 Broadway, New York, NY 10003

MC/Visa orders may be
telephoned to (603) 669-5933.

The Wisdom of Milton H. Erickson
Volume 2, Human Behavior & Psychotherapy

Ronald A. Havens, Editor

Milton H. Erickson was one of the most creative, dynamic, and effective hypnotherapists and psychotherapists of the twentieth century. Erickson's books have sold more than 250,000 copies. He used unconventional techniques with remarkable success. An indication of the respect Erickson gained from his peers are the words inscribed on his 1976 Benjamin Franklin Gold Medal, the highest award that the International Society of Clinical and Experimental Hypnosis can bestow: "To Milton H. Erickson, M.D.—innovator, outstanding clinician, and distinguished investigator whose ideas have not only helped create the modern view of hypnosis but have profoundly influenced the practice of all psychotherapy throughout the world."

Although he wrote hundreds of papers, articles, and books in his lifetime, Erickson himself never put his techniques and methods into a clear and centralized body of work. *The Wisdom of Milton H. Erickson, II: Human Behavior and Psychotherapy* is an effort to do just that. Along with its companion volume, *The Wisdom of Milton H. Erickson I: Hypnosis and Hypnotherapy*, this book is a collection of Erickson's methods and lessons, including his feelings on the uses of objective observation, the uniqueness of the conscious mind, the realities and abilities of the unconscious mind, the creation and use of a therapeutic environment, and many other aspects of the life and work of this remarkable thinker and teacher.

...a heroic effort to bring clarity to a hard-to-grasp theory...(This book) is a major reference for students and scholars who want to know what Erickson said and when and where he said it.

Contemporary Psychology

ISBN 0-8290-2414-X (Paper)
258 pages
$14.95

IRVINGTON PUBLISHERS, INC.
740 Broadway, New York, NY 10003

MC/Visa orders may be
telephoned to (603) 669-5933.

NOW AVAILABLE

Principles of Self Hypnosis
Pathways to the Unconscious

by C. Alexander Simpkins, Ph.D. and Annellen M. Simpkins, Ph.D.

Most self hypnosis books are incomplete. They show readers how to use their conscious mind to dominate the unconscious mind but fail to deal with the unconscious directly. In this book, the reader is shown how to experiment with the unconscious mind, unfettered by the conscious mind when appropriate. Trance is used with conscious direct suggestion, unconscious indirect suggestion, and induced free flow of associations.

The book offers an in depth history of hypnosis with special emphasis on the development of self hypnosis. Readers are also given information on the unconscious, learning, mind/body, and other topics to help them understand and creatively use self hypnosis.

Exercises throughout can be used verbatim or as guidelines for the reader's own creative associations.

An unusually lucid presentation and integration! The authors present ways to apply the techniques developed in the book to common applications and they consistently use the therapeutic trance as the primary source for learning.

Ernest L. Rossi, Ph.D., Editor of
The Collected Papers of Milton H. Erickson

ISBN 0-8290-2415-8 (Cloth)
234 pages
$19.95

FOR ORDER FORM SEE PAGE 275 OF THIS BOOK

IRVINGTON PUBLISHERS, INC.
740 Broadway, New York, NY 10003

MC/Visa orders may be telephoned to (603) 669-5933.